Welcome to the Ultimate Guide to Samsung Galaxy

Samsung's Galaxy range of devices are amongst the best-selling in 2012, and no doubt will continue to top the charts throughout 2013 and beyond.

Welcome to the Samsung Galaxy MagBook - a resource to help you choose which Samsung Galaxy device is best for you if you're thinking of entering the Galaxy ecosystem. And, of course, how to use it once you've got it home.

This comprehensive guide, written by the Know Your Mobile team of experts, will help you along the way with your Galaxy device, whether you're using a smartphone, tablet or a phablet.

This MagBook has been designed for every type of user, from those who want to know how to set up their Samsung Galaxy device, to those who need more advanced instruction.

With the Know Your Mobile team's app recommendations and top secret tips, you can be sure you're getting the best insight into Galaxy devices, from those who have been using them for a long period of time.

We guarantee you'll come away knowing exactly how to do anything on your Samsung Galaxy device, whether you want to develop your own app, take better pictures or just want to know how to get the most out of Maps.

Clare Hopping
Group editor, Know Your Mobile

Chapter 1

Introduction to Galaxy

Chapter 2

Devices

Chapter 3

Setting up your Galaxy

Chapter 4

Applications

Chapter 5

Photography

Chapter 6

Music and multimedia

Contributors
Editor Clare Hopping
Contributors Paul Briden, Richard Goodwin, Basil Kronfli
Sub editor Maggie Holland
Designer Leon David

Management
MagBook Publisher Dharmesh Mistry
Digital Production Manager Nicky Baker
Operations Director Robin Ryan
Managing Director of Advertising Julian Lloyd-Evans
Newstrade Director David Barker
Chief Operating Officer Brett Reynolds
Group Finance Director Ian Leggett
Chief Executive James Tye
Chairman Felix Dennis

MAG**BOOK**™

The Ultimate Guide to Samsung Galaxy
[ISBN 1-78106-182-3]

Licensing
To license this product, please contact Carlotta Serantoni on +44 (0) 20 7907 6550 or email carlotta_serantoni@dennis.co.uk.
To syndicate content from this product please contact Anj Dosaj Halai on +44 (0) 20 7907 6132 or email anj_dosaj-halai@dennis.co.uk.

The paper used within this MagBook is produced from sustainable fibre, manufactured by mills with a valid chain of custody. Printed at BGP Bicester.

Chapter 1

Introduction to Samsung Galaxy

Introduction to Samsung Galaxy

Samsung's Galaxy range covers a broad selection of smartphone and tablet devices, but the one thing they all have in common is Google's Android operating system.

The range began with the original Samsung Galaxy smartphone but it was the Samsung Galaxy S premium model which really put the company's brand of Android hardware on the map.

Since then, it has expanded to include budget, mid-range and further premium models, some of which are the highest-selling mobile devices on the market today.

The Samsung Galaxy portfolio includes a wide range of smartphones from the Galaxy Ace and Galaxy Y, to recently released high-end models such as the Galaxy S III.

Samsung has also created some quirky and pioneering purpose-specific models: the Samsung Galaxy Beam, for example, incorporates a projector, while the Galaxy Note series includes smartphones and tablets with unique S-Pen stylus capabilities.

Each Samsung Galaxy device runs Android aswell as a custom interface overlay known as TouchWiz, which introduces a number of Samsung's tailored features. There are specialised settings, menus and interface elements as well as a Samsung visual style for app icons and themes.

Android is currently one of the most prolific and well-supported mobile operating systems in the world and, at last count, had more than 700,000 apps in the Google Play store, with more being added every day.

In the next section, we'll show you how the Galaxy range has evolved, the different versions of Android from one model to the next and the variations of Samsung's TouchWiz user interface (UI) overlay.

Samsung Galaxy timeline

2009

June 2009
Samsung Galaxy launched as first Samsung Galaxy Android smartphone

2010

June 2010
Samsung Galaxy S flagship launched

November 2010
Samsung Galaxy Tab launched

2011

May 2011
Samsung Galaxy S II launched

June 2011
Samsung Galaxy Tab 10.1 launched

August 2011
Samsung Galaxy S Plus launched

October 2011
Samsung Galaxy Note launched as first S-Pen stylus-driven 5-inch smartphone

November 2011
Samsung Galaxy Nexus launched as first Samsung-made Google Nexus handset

2012

April 2012
Samsung Galaxy S Advance launched

May 2012
Samsung Galaxy S III flagship launched

July 2012
Android Jelly Bean 4.1 arrived for Galaxy Nexus. Android Ice Cream Sandwich 4.0 update rolled out for Galaxy S II and Galaxy Note

August 2012
Samsung Galaxy Note 10.1 launched. Galaxy Tab range updated to Android Ice Cream Sandwich 4.0

October 2012
Samsung Galaxy Note II launched. Android Jelly Bean 4.1 update rolled out for Galaxy S III

November 2012
Android Jelly Bean 4.1 update rolled out for Galaxy Note 10.1

2012-2013

December 2012-February 2013
Android 4.2 rolled out to Samsung Galaxy, Galaxy S III and Galaxy Note 2

Explaining Android versions

Android 2.1

Eclair

Android 2.1 Eclair is the earliest build of Android you'll find on Samsung Galaxy phones, although most can now be upgraded to at least 2.2 Froyo or higher.

Eclair brought with it deeper account syncing than previous versions, allowing users to add a wider variety of email and social networking accounts, including Exchange email support and merged inbox capability.

This is also the version where contact cards became richer and infinitely more usable, with call, text and email options all in one place, along with a variety of other interactions. Messaging also benefits from a search function and an auto-delete toggle for old messages.

The browser's updated interface is improved with a double-tap zoom function and HTML5 support. Overall system performance and interface responsiveness is better than earlier builds too.

Android 2.2

Froyo

Android 2.2 Froyo is still in circulation on some early models (now largely budget-priced) handsets in the Galaxy range. While there are models that ship with 2.1 Eclair, most can be immediately upgraded to Froyo straight out of the box.

It's faster, more efficient and more stable than its predecessors and Google also added a customisable search bar allowing you to choose whether the phone searches apps, contacts, the internet, or all three. Phone and browser shortcuts are included in the main navigation bar for quick and easy access.

The built-in browser speed is faster than before, while phones running this build support USB and Wi-Fi Hotspot tethering. Froyo also allows for microSD storage to be used for app installation and app data.

In terms of security, you have the option of using a PIN, password or gesture lock. Microsoft Exchange email support was updated to include options for security policies, calendar synchronisation and remote wipe, amongst many others. You can also toggle mobile network data access on or off.

Android 2.3

Gingerbread

Version 2.3 Gingerbread's interface layout, design and controls are much slicker and more intuitive than earlier builds, while performance and reliability is also improved.

An app management suite gives users greater control over installed apps and over running apps at any given time.

This also incorporates an active app manager feature where the operating system monitors activity and shuts off apps which hog system resources. A download manager has also been added to help you keep track of files, apps and the like.

Devices with Gingerbread and above can use their gyroscopes and motion sensors with compatible motion control games.

The touch keyboard has recieved an overhaul and is much easier to use and the operating system natively supports an enhanced copy and paste function at all levels.

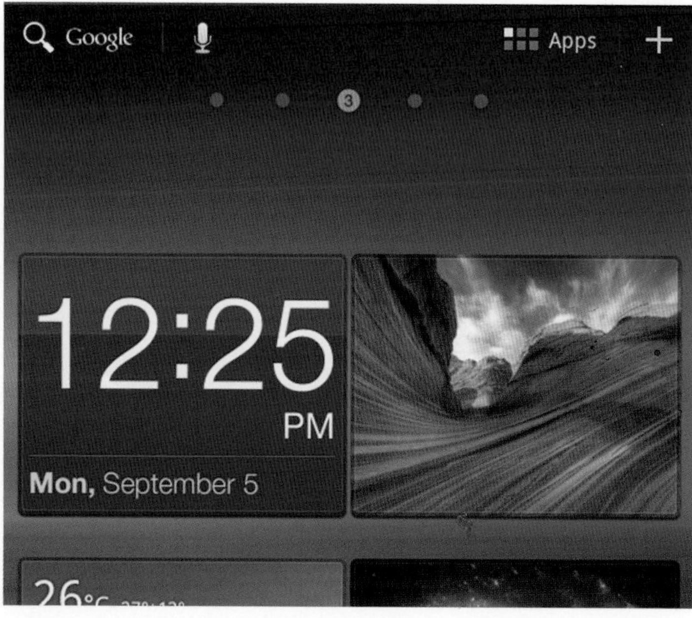

3.2

Android 3.2

Honeycomb

Honeycomb was specifically engineered for tablets and most devices running it can now immediately be updated to at least version 4.0 Ice cream Sandwich (ICS).

However, it was also the beginning of Android's excellent 'Holo' UI, which gave everything some much-needed spit and polish. Once again, performance was improved compared to earlier versions.

Notably, Honeycomb bought the touch-keyboard in-line with rival offerings in terms of fluidity, accuracy and responsiveness. This was also the first version to introduce the highly useful multitasking carousel.

The interface is also well-optimised for the tablet format thanks to an emphasis on thumb control and the fact that all notifications are put in a combined settings and notification menu, which is highly detailed with system information.

Browser performance has been improved hugely too, as well as introducing tabbed browsing.

Explaining Android versions

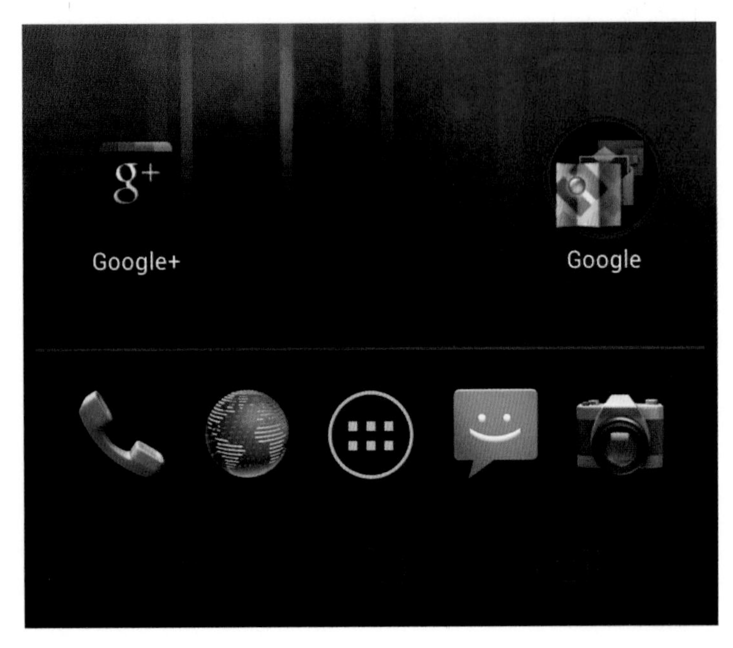

Android 4.0

Ice Cream Sandwich

Android 4.0 builds significantly on previous versions. Performance is incredibly quick, even on devices which struggled with Gingerbread and earlier iterations, stability is also excellent and really brings Android up to speed with its rivals.

The update is more significant for smartphones as it extends some of the previously tablet-only Honeycomb features to more devices.

Primarily, this comes in the form of interface tweaks, a cohesive visual style and the multitasking carousel for quickly switching between apps. There's also a newly added swipe-to-close feature, giving you greater control on the surface. This is also the first time Android smartphones gained a settings menu shortcut in the notifications bar.

4.1 4.2

Android 4.1/4.2

Jelly Bean

Jelly Bean took performance and stability even further and overall system smoothness was greatly enhanced. The addition of the Butter UI means the display synchronises with the operating system to provide seamless visuals and touch responsiveness with virtually no latency. Notifications are now expandable, for more detail at a glance, while the swipe-to-close function now exists in many other UI areas outside of the multitasking carousel.

Jelly Bean also introduced Google Now, a notification service which merges Google Search, Google Maps and Google Voice into a unified platform. This provides useful information relevant to your regular commutes, weather reports, local points of interest and much more. The voice component is one of the best on the market too.

Jelly Bean 4.2 enhances Google Now even further and adds a second drop-down 'quick settings' menu to the notifications bar, which allows you to quickly toggle key settings such as Wi-Fi. Photosphere allows you to take 360-degree panoramic photos and upload them to Google Maps, while Miracast lets you stream content to HD-enabled TVs.

Explaining TouchWiz versions

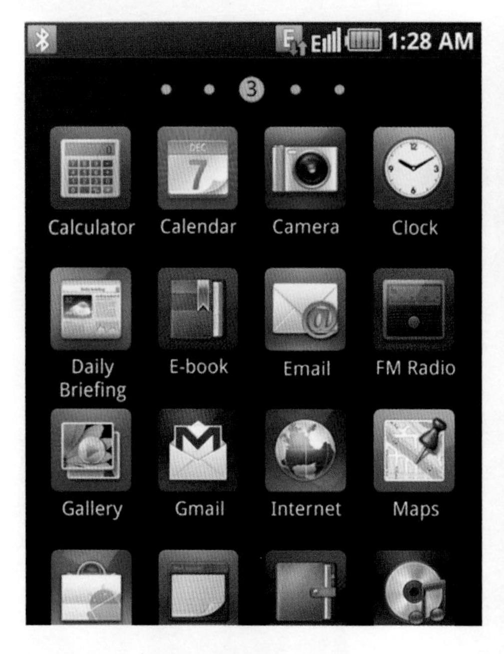

TouchWiz 3.0

TouchWiz 3.0 makes a number of changes to the standard Android interface.

The lock screen allows you to swipe anywhere to unlock the device, while the drop-down notifications menu features a number of quick-settings toggles for Wi-Fi, mobile data and other commonly used functions.

Samsung has expanded the default number of homescreens from three to a maximum of seven, though you can customise how many you want. The App Drawer has been tweaked and now features a horizontally scrolling set of 4x4 grid 'pages' rather than regular Android's continuous vertical setup.

Wallpapers, themes and app shortcuts all have a unique Samsung flavour and the default number of widgets has been expanded too.

TouchWiz 4.0

TouchWiz 4.0 brings some new visual changes with it. Across the board, there's more transparency and gradients to make things look a bit more clean and modern. Icons and the keyboard skin have also been updated.

The first three dock shortcuts (everything except the App Drawer shortcut) can now be swapped out with whatever you like. Text messages are also now threaded, allowing you to keep track of conversations more easily.

Samsung has added a number of hubs for various functions. These include the Social Hub, Game Hub, Music Hub and Readers Hub.

The camera interface has been streamlined and made largely transparent, so you can see more of the image you're capturing. You can also select up to five commonly used camera feature shortcuts for quick access. Photo and video editing suites also come bundled with the software.

TouchWiz UX

TouchWiz UX, also known as the 'Nature' interface, can be found on Samsung's most recent devices such as the Galaxy S III and Note 2. The visual design has been overhauled completely with custom nature-themed wallpapers and sounds, an animated lock screen swipe and menu elements which have been brought in-line with the style of Android version 4.0 and onwards.

Many new Samsung apps are tied into the interface, such as S Voice, the Video Hub and Samsung's take on Google Calendar, S Planner.

The quick-settings function in the drop-down menu now includes more toggles and is scrollable from side-to-side. There's also a brightness control slider for immediate access.

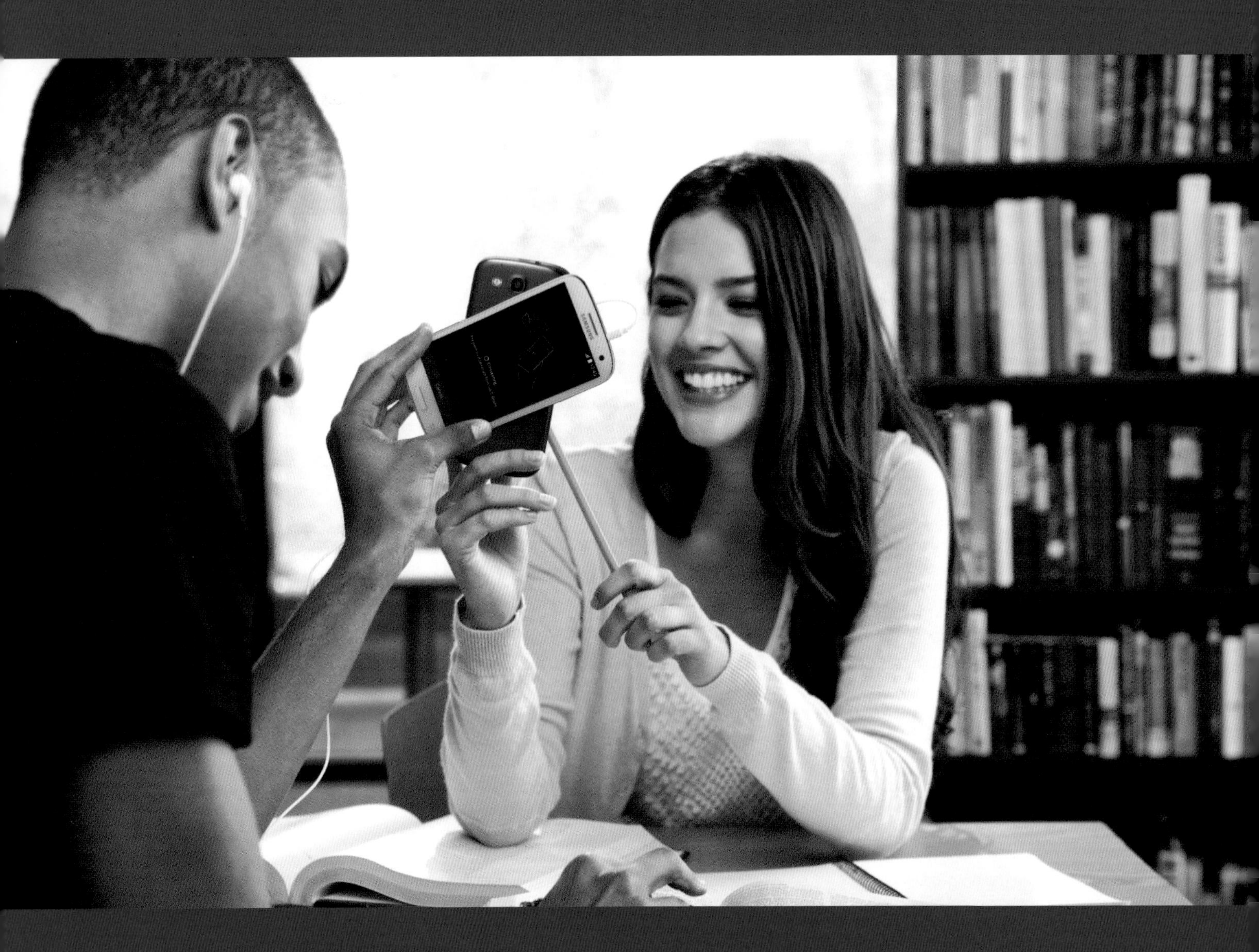

Chapter 2

Devices

Samsung Galaxy S II

As the successor to the commercially popular, iPhone-inspired Galaxy S, the S II always had its work cut out. Samsung obviously knew this, as during the lengthy wait from its unveiling at Mobile World Congress 2011 to its launch, the dual-core processor was upped from 1GHz to 1.2GHz.

With 4.3-inches of Super AMOLED+ display - the latest version of Samsung's own screen technology - viewing web pages, games, apps and images is physically easier. Colours are beautifully vivid too. In fact, Angry Birds has never looked so good.

The chassis itself is also impressive. The Galaxy S could be confused with the iPhone 3G and 3GS, whereas the S II stands on its own two feet in the design stakes.

Those of you who like to take the odd photo will be pleased to know the S II once again comes up trumps - the 8-megapixel camera is one of the best we tested in 2011.

What the Galaxy S II lacks in a metal finish, it makes up for with sheer hardware power. It offers a big screen, a powerful processor, plenty of memory, a great camera and lengthy battery life - a fine Android experience overall.

ANNOUNCED
February 2011

CONTRACT PRICE
Free from £16.50 per month

PREPAY PRICE
£299

SIZE
125.3 x 66.1 x 8.5mm

WEIGHT
116g

SCREEN SIZE
4.3-inches

STORAGE
16/32GB

CAMERA
8-megapixels

PROCESSOR
Dual-core 1.2GHz Cortex-A9

BATTERY LIFE
610 hours standby
8.5 hours talktime

ANDROID VERSION
Gingerbread, version 2.3.4, upgradeable to Jelly Bean version 4.1

Samsung Galaxy S III

The Galaxy S III was always going to cause a stir. By releasing the best Android phone of 2011 in the form of the Galaxy S II, the bar was automatically set very high, which then caused what we now affectionately call iPhone 4 syndrome: where users end up having very unrealistic expectations.

A 4.8-inch display is certainly not small, but the Galaxy S III manages to house it exceptionally well. In typical Samsung style, you get Super AMOLED technology, which means colours are vibrant and everything has a warm colour about it.

We did find the large screen was more prone to picking up reflections, especially when the sun comes out, and the smooth back panel is quite slippy too. We also still secretly pined for casing like on the HTC One X. You can't beat a bit of metal on a premium device.

Android 4.0 has come on leaps and bounds so we would definitely now recommend it to smartphone newbies as well as the tech-massive who love tinkering.

It's not quite perfect and we feel a lot of the Samsung-added functionality is a little gimmicky, plus more could have been made of the natural theme, but it really doesn't matter when the rest of the device works so well.

If you want the essence of the Samsung Galaxy S II with more oomph or one of the best Android devices of 2012, the Galaxy S III is for you.

ANNOUNCED
May 2012

CONTRACT PRICE
From free for £25 per month

PREPAY PRICE
£430

SIZE
136.6 x 70.6 x 8.6mm

WEIGHT
133g

SCREEN SIZE
4.8-inches

STORAGE
16/32/64GB

CAMERA
8-megapixel

PROCESSOR
Quad-core 1.4GHz Cortex-A9

BATTERY LIFE
790 hours standby
11.5 hours talktime

ANDROID VERSION
Jelly Bean, version 4.1, upgradeable to 4.2

Samsung Galaxy S III Mini

The Samsung Galaxy S III Mini is the pint-sized sibling of the Samsung Galaxy S III and, as such, some of the features have been streamlined.

First up, the screen measures 4-inches, which is significantly smaller than the Samsung Galaxy S III. Then again, it's only going back to the same size as the original Samsung Galaxy S so probably isn't a deal breaker.

The processor has been scaled down to a 1GHz chip, which doesn't give nearly the same oomph as the device's bigger brother, but with a smaller screen to power, it's not as severe an issue as you may think. What's more, it doesn't stutter or lag, but that's with only a handful of apps running.

Samsung also seems to have taken its foot off the gas when it comes to design. It's smaller than the Galaxy S III, but also - curiously - thicker at 9.9mm.

The camera is 5-megapixels and is a noticeable step down from the powerhouse snapper the Galaxy S III featured.

Storage options are 8GB or 16GB, which isn't too shabby on a device that will cost you nothing on a £15-per-month contract.

Although the Samsung Galaxy S III Mini may appeal to those with a lighter budget, it doesn't come close to the quality and feature set of the rest of the Galaxy S series family.

ANNOUNCED
October 2012

CONTRACT PRICE
Free from £15 per month

PREPAY PRICE
£295

SIZE
121.6 x 63 x 9.9mm

WEIGHT
111.5g

SCREEN SIZE
4-inches

STORAGE
8/16 GB

CAMERA
5-megapixels

PROCESSOR
Dual-core 1GHz

BATTERY LIFE
430 hours standby
7 hours talktime

ANDROID VERSION
Jelly Bean, version 4.1

Samsung Galaxy S Advance

The Galaxy S Advance comes with Android 2.3 and TouchWiz 4.0, which is by no means bad but there are many more powerful alternatives out there such as the HTC One V and the Sony Xperia S.

Being a slightly smaller Galaxy S II and a more powerful Galaxy Advance means the performance is great for a mid-range device. It also means you get a relatively lightweight plastic chassis.

With 768MB of RAM, a dual-core Cortex-A9 processor and either 8GB or 16GB of storage, it's a nifty little mover when it comes to user experience.

The resolution of 480x800 pixels, which gives a pixel density of 233ppi, provides enough detail for anyone but the most tech-savvy punter and the 4-inch size has enough impact to keep you glued to it.

Alas, we've seen so many recent handsets released with little thought for where Android is going, and the S Advance is no different. A year ago we would've been impressed but nowadays it's a tad overpriced for what you get.

You would be better off saving up a little and going for the now Jelly Bean-equipped Galaxy S II, which has a better camera, faster processor, better chassis and a longer future. It's not that the S Advance is bad, it's just a by-product of such a fast moving platform.

ANNOUNCED
January 2012

CONTRACT PRICE
Free from £25 per month

PREPAY PRICE
Not available

SIZE
123.2 x 63 x 9.7mm

WEIGHT
120g

SCREEN SIZE
4-inches

STORAGE
8/16GB

CAMERA
5-megapixels

PROCESSOR
Dual-core 1GHz Cortex-A9

BATTERY LIFE
550 hours standby
7.5 hours talktime

ANDROID VERSION
Gingerbread, version 2.3, upgradeable to Jelly Bean, version 4.1

Samsung Galaxy Nexus

Samsung's Galaxy Nexus continues on with the untouched Android experience, only this time Gingerbread has crumbled away to leave room for Ice Cream Sandwich out-of-the-box. It's also upgradeable to Jelly Bean version 4.2.

One of the Galaxy Nexus' finest areas is its display. In addition to being fairly large, it's also very bright and incredibly vivid.

A mixture of lightweight materials and a relatively thin profile keep the Galaxy Nexus from looking and feeling too big. Besides feeling a bit plasticky, the Galaxy Nexus is designed very well and is surprisingly pocketable. Indeed, compared to the Galaxy Note, this feels very compact.

Thanks to the removal of hardware or permanent touch buttons, the front view is very sleek and there's minimal edging around the sizeable 4.65-inch Super AMOLED HD screen.

As a Google-branded device, the Galaxy Nexus is top of the Samsung pile. Performance is quick, the camera is tip top and build quality is to die for. Another advantage of the Galaxy Nexus is it's always the first device to get firmware updates, such as Android Jelly Bean 4.2, which is a massive improvement over Ice Cream Sandwich that comes pre-installed on the device.

ANNOUNCED
October 2011

CONTRACT PRICE
Free from £17 a month

PREPAY PRICE
£480

SIZE
135.5 x 67.9 x 8.9mm

WEIGHT
135g

SCREEN SIZE
4.65-inches

STORAGE
16GB

CAMERA
5-megapixels

PROCESSOR
Dual-core 1.2GHz Cortex-A9

BATTERY LIFE
270 hours standby
8 hours talktime

ANDROID VERSION
Ice Cream Sandwich, version 4.0, upgradeable to Jelly Bean, version 4.2

Samsung Galaxy Beam

Rumours surrounding a Samsung projector phone have been doing the rounds for years. Then, finally, an Android-powered projector phone was launched - albeit a SIM-free version.

The Samsung Galaxy Beam runs on a fairly standard upper mid-range set of specifications. We've got a dual-core 1GHz processor and 8GB of internal storage at the heart of things.

Considering the Samsung Galaxy Beam has a projector on board, Samsung hasn't paid a huge amount of attention to its cameras. The main snapper shoots at 5-megapixels, and has an LED flash, and the front camera has a 1.3-megapixel lens.

The projector, on the other hand, is fun - though it does have its limitations. It projects onto any surface at a resolution of 640x360 in full colour and Samsung has bundled a handful of apps to make the most of this feature.

The Samsung Galaxy Beam is a competent smartphone, though the version of Android supported is a bit of a let down. Its two batteries give it superb longevity and its physical design is attractive. The projector is a bit of a gimmick but it works well within its limitations of projection size and darkness requirements.

Of course, you pay for that projector and the Beam is a bit more expensive than other handsets with similar general specs.

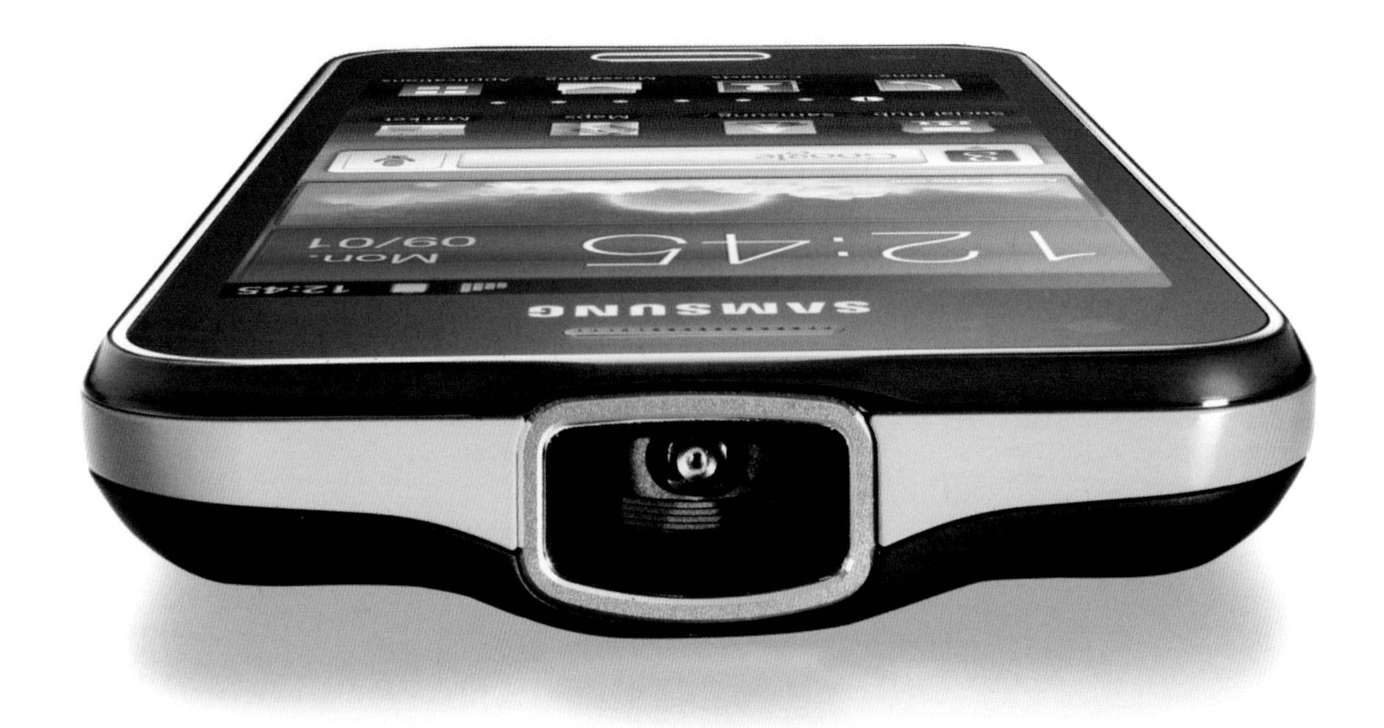

ANNOUNCED
February 2012

CONTRACT PRICE
Free from £26 per month

PREPAY PRICE
Not available

SIZE
124 x 64.2 x 12.5mm

WEIGHT
145.3g

SCREEN SIZE
4-inches

STORAGE
8GB

CAMERA
5-megapixels

PROCESSOR
Dual-core 1GHz Cortex-A9

BATTERY LIFE
760 hours standby
9.5 hours talktime

ANDROID VERSION
Gingerbread, version 2.3.6 upgradeable to Jelly Bean version 4.1

Samsung Galaxy Ace 2

The Samsung Galaxy Ace 2 continues on from the success of the Samsung Galaxy Ace, but it adds a heap of improved features that make it a viable option for those looking for a low-cost Android Samsung device.

The processor has been upped to dual-core from single-core, the screen to 3.8-inches - although it's still not to the same standard as those premium handsets - and the battery life has been given a little boost too. It also boasts a higher resolution at 480x800 pixels, which makes the screen crisper and brighter than the first version of this mid to low-ender.

Storage has been beefed up - from 158MB to 4GB, - and, although it's not the same as 16GB, microSD cards will help house your music collection.

What we're most impressed by though, is that it is upgradeable to Android Jelly Bean 4.1, which is an amazing operating system compared to Gingerbread, which the device ships with.

Adding the Butter UI, it's super smooth to run, even though there's only an 800MHz processor (albeit dual-core), which certainly impressed us.

The casing is a little plasticky, which won't wow the style conscious, and the screen is still a little too small for comfortable typing or web browsing, but it's all in a decent package, for very little money on prepay.

ANNOUNCED
February 2012

CONTRACT PRICE
Free from £15.50 per month

PREPAY PRICE
£160

SIZE
118.3 x 62.2 x 10.5mm

WEIGHT
122g

SCREEN SIZE
3.8-inches

STORAGE
4GB

CAMERA
5-megapixels

PROCESSOR
Dual-core 800MHz

BATTERY LIFE
640 hours standby
7.5 hours talktime

ANDROID VERSION
Gingerbread, version 2.3, upgradeable to Jelly Bean, version 4.1

Samsung Galaxy Pocket

The Samsung Galaxy Pocket is a true low-end device with an absolutely tiny 2.8-inch touchscreen at a rather low resolution of 320x480 pixels.

This screen would probably put the Galaxy Pocket in the feature phone category, but the operating system is the one thing that separates the dinky device from such a tag.

Rather surprisingly for a device launched in 2012, the Galaxy Pocket runs on Android Gingerbread version 2.3, hand-in-hand with Touchwiz. For a device with an 832MHz processor, it really should just be vanilla Android to try and save some of that processing power for apps rather than a skin.

That said, it runs pretty well, mostly because that screen is *so* small.

Wi-Fi and 3G are both present and correct, but we would recommend you stay far away from browsing – the screen just isn't designed for it.

Simple apps like Facebook and mobile websites run more than adequately though and 3GB of internal storage will give you enough space for a fair few apps.

Multimedia is as you would expect from a phone costing £10.50 a month, with a 2-megapixel camera and crackly speakers – it's just a shame the device isn't available on prepay any longer.

The Samsung Galaxy Pocket will certainly slide into a pocket of any size and we would say it's particularly suitable for young children, or at least those with tiny fingers who only want to use the device for calling, texting and a limited amount of app usage.

ANNOUNCED
February 2012

CONTRACT PRICE
Free from £10.50 a month

PREPAY PRICE
No longer available

SIZE
103.7 x 57.5 x 12mm

WEIGHT
97g

SCREEN SIZE
2.8-inches

STORAGE
3GB

CAMERA
2-megapixels

PROCESSOR
832MHz ARM 11

BATTERY LIFE
500 hours standby
5.5 hours talktime

ANDROID VERSION
Gingerbread, version 2.3

Samsung Galaxy Mini 2

The Galaxy Mini 2 is the successor to Samsung's previous budget Android offering the Galaxy Mini. Like all good sequels, it has been blessed with enhanced internals and a more appealing design.

Despite its diminutive size, the Galaxy Mini 2 feels sturdy and dependable, which could be another plus if you're buying this handset for a younger, perhaps clumsier, family member.

Its 800MHz processor isn't the fastest challenger on the block, but the phone generally copes well with daily tasks and while it would be foolish to expect dual-core power in such a modest device, the recent proliferation of 1GHz budget handsets could make it hard for the Galaxy Mini 2 to carve a niche for itself.

The final thing worthy of note is the inclusion of Near Field Communications (NFC) technology. This contactless method of exchanging information is becoming more and more popular on mobile phones. It allows you to make payments, exchange data with other phones and even trigger events on your device when using a specially-formatted NFC tag.

The Galaxy Mini 2 is a solid successor to the original Galaxy Mini, but the competition in this sector of the Android market has intensified over the past year, so it might have trouble keeping its cheaper rivals at bay.

ANNOUNCED
February 2012

CONTRACT PRICE
Free from £10.50 a month

PREPAY PRICE
£110

SIZE
109.4 x 58.6 x 11.6mm

WEIGHT
105g

SCREEN SIZE
3.3-inches

STORAGE
4GB

CAMERA
3.15-megapixels

PROCESSOR
800MHz Cortex-A5

BATTERY LIFE
420 hours standby
6.5 hours talktime

ANDROID VERSION
Gingerbread, version 2.3

Samsung Galaxy Music

The Samsung Galaxy Music is designed to be a top-class music mobile, with tunes at the top of its agenda.

The Galaxy Music is available in a range of vibrant colours and features a metal trim. There's a grille at the top and the bottom for speakers – somewhat expected on a music-focused mobile, but useful nonetheless.

There are also dedicated music controls around the edges – again, something you'd expect to find on a device marketed as music-centric.

The 3.3-inch screen has a rather disappointing 240x320 pixel resolution, which certainly isn't suitable for playing videos.

Touchwiz UI is overlaid on Android Ice Cream Sandwich, and it runs pretty well with an 850MHz single-core Cortex-A9 processor against similar-specced handsets.

Unfortunately, 4GB of internal storage isn't really enough for a device designed for tunes on the move, so you will have to invest in a microSD card to boost your collection. The slot is hot-swappable though so it's very quick and easy to switch between different cards.

Available as an O2 exclusive at the time of writing with a price tag of £110 on prepay, the Samsung Galaxy Music is certainly one aimed at the youth market. With two pretty decent speakers and music hardware buttons, it does exactly what it says on the tin.

ANNOUNCED
October 2012

CONTRACT PRICE
Free from £29 a month

PREPAY PRICE
£110

SIZE
110.1 x 59 x 12.3mm

WEIGHT
106.9g

SCREEN SIZE
3.3-inches

STORAGE
4GB

CAMERA
3.15-megapixels

PROCESSOR
850MHz

BATTERY LIFE
420 hours standby
6.5 hours talktime

ANDROID VERSION
Ice Cream Sandwich, version 4.0.4, upgradeable to Jelly Bean, version 4.1

Samsung Galaxy Note

Samsung was keen to give the Galaxy Note a mighty list of specs. Beneath its giant exterior is a suitably big 1.4GHz dual-core processor. But, even so, the real-world experience isn't quite as smooth when jumping between the seven home screens and it does occasionally stall.

Fortunately, loading times are very good, although once you get into using a stylus, the Note definitely feels a little slower than other premium devices.

The big screen is perfect for video playback, viewing websites and gaming. The Note's features, however, aren't up to the standard of the Note II. The 5.3-inch AMOLED HD screen did mean we were able to write the odd thing here and there, but certainly not a novel or essay.

The Note is a very similar device to the Samsung Galaxy S II, but with an extra stylus, larger screen and a few extra bells and whistles. It has positioned itself into an awkward niche. It's too small to cope with the tablet market but too big to hang around with the smartphone crowd.

If you loved the Galaxy S II but wanted a massive display, the Note will be money well spent, especially as it's remarkably cheaper than the much better Galaxy Note II.

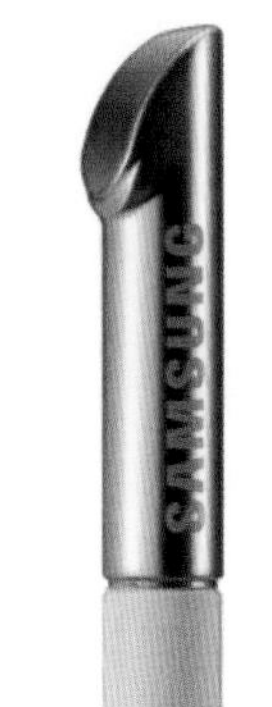

ANNOUNCED
September 2011

CONTRACT PRICE
From free for £20.50 per month

PREPAY PRICE
£380

SIZE
146.9 x 83 x 9.7mm

WEIGHT
178g

SCREEN SIZE
5.3-inches

STORAGE
8/16GB

CAMERA
5-megapixels

PROCESSOR
1GHz Cortex-A8

BATTERY LIFE
820 hours standby
13.5 hours talktime

ANDROID VERSION
Gingerbread, version 2.3, upgradeable to version 4.1

Samsung Galaxy Note II

This is a great offering from Samsung, but as with previous Galaxy Note devices it will not suit everyone's tastes.

There is still the issue of whether or not you feel comfortable making calls on a phone of this size too. You've essentially got three options: you can either be the confident type and hold it to your face as if everything is normal, you can rely entirely on the speakerphone or you can just make sure you've got a hands-free kit with you at all times.

With moderate use we found the sizeable 3100mAh battery will last a couple of days with no trouble at all. However, once you start factoring in intensive gaming sessions or heavy use of the stylus functionality, things can start to drain off alarmingly quickly.

With a quad-core processor and an additional gigabyte of RAM the Galaxy Note II is a much more capable stylus-based handset.

We much prefer the implementation of the stylus features here, mainly because the Note II is so much better at letting you write smoothly and accurately – it even recognises when you rest your palm on the screen and doesn't allow it to interrupt you.

Is it perfect? Of course not. But, it is unquestionably the best realisation of the Galaxy Note concept we've seen so far.

ANNOUNCED
August 2012

CONTRACT PRICE
Free from £29 per month

PREPAY PRICE
£480

SIZE
151.1 x 80.5 x 9.4mm

WEIGHT
183g

SCREEN SIZE
5.5-inches

STORAGE
16/32/64GB

CAMERA
8-megapixels

PROCESSOR
Quad-core 1.6GHz Cortex-A9

BATTERY LIFE
890 hours standby
16 hours talktime

ANDROID VERSION
Jelly Bean, version 4.1, upgradeable to version 4.2

Samsung Galaxy Note 10.1

The Galaxy Note 10.1 is a highly competent tablet, which is only flawed by some of its snazzy and overambitious new features.

The 1280x800 pixel resolution is reasonably pleasing to the eye and Samsung has managed to churn out some impressive colours, contrast and brightness.

The Galaxy Note 10.1 runs on Samsung's own Exynos 4412 quad-core chip, based on ARM's Cortex-A9 architecture, clocked at 1.4GHz with 2GB of RAM and a powerful Mali-400MP graphics processing unit (GPU).

Other noteworthy hardware elements include the onboard storage space, which comes in three flavours depending on price: 16GB, 32GB and 64GB.

The S-Pen functionality has moved on from that of the original Galaxy Note. The sensitivity is miles better, both in terms of pin-point precision and in how quickly it picks up your movements.

For the purposes it is intended to fulfil it should do very well on the whole, but anyone wishing to buy one should be aware that it will be a trial and error learning experience that makes you fit around the tablet rather than the other way around.

If you're thinking of getting the Note 10.1 as a productivity tool, it certainly can cater to your needs, but you'll need to bear in mind that battery consumption can run away from you, certain S-Pen related apps may lag and the multiscreen, while a great idea, doesn't perform so well in practice.

ANNOUNCED
August 2012

CONTRACT PRICE
N/A, from £325 SIM free

PREPAY PRICE
N/A

SIZE
262 x 180 x 8.9mm

WEIGHT
600g

SCREEN SIZE
10.1-inches

STORAGE
16/32/64GB

CAMERA
5-megapixels

PROCESSOR
Quad-core 1.4GHz Cortex-A9

BATTERY LIFE
1500 hours standby
33 hours talktime

ANDROID VERSION
Ice Cream Sandwich, version 4.0.3 upgradeable to version 4.1

Samsung Galaxy Tab

A whole horde of Android-based tablets were announced following the successful launch of the Apple iPad. The Samsung Galaxy Tab is not only the first of these Android tablets to actually go on sale, but it's also one of the most hyped and eagerly awaited since Samsung's Galaxy S smartphone.

Although the Tab's 7-inch screen uses an LCD instead of an AMOLED panel like the Galaxy S, it's still very bright and vivid looking.

Typing on the Tab's onscreen keyboard works surprisingly well. When oriented vertically, we were able to type with our thumbs quite accurately.

Surprisingly, Samsung hasn't completely skinned Android with its own TouchWiz interface familiar to Galaxy S owners - it's just the App Drawer that gets a TouchWiz-style makeover.

The Samsung Galaxy Tab is a lot like Christmas. After all the anticipation, in reality it's a bit of a let down. Although the Tab is a sturdy, slender, lightweight and attractive tablet, it could be easier to hold. The Tab's small size, which makes it great for reading, also makes it less suitable for writing judging from our experiences with the onscreen keyboard.

Even more critically, it's let down badly by the sluggish interface. Other frustrating aspects of operating system, such as copy and paste, lead us to believe that Android 2.2 isn't ideally suited for tablets. We really want to like the Tab, but until a software update comes out that fixes the Tab's problems - perhaps Android 3.0 Gingerbread - we'd still rather have an iPad.

ANNOUNCED
September 2010

CONTRACT PRICE
N/A, from £375 SIM free

PREPAY PRICE
No longer available

SIZE
190.1 x 120.5 x 12mm

WEIGHT
380g

SCREEN SIZE
7-inches

STORAGE
16/32GB

CAMERA
3.15-megapixels

PROCESSOR
1GHz Cortex A8

BATTERY LIFE
1200 hours standby
25 hours talktime

ANDROID VERSION
Froyo, version 2.2 upgradeable to version 2.3

Samsung Galaxy Tab 8.9

The Samsung Galaxy Tab 8.9 is a smaller version of the original Galaxy Tab and many believe this is the perfect size for a tablet.

The 8.9-inch, 1280x800 pixel screen is bright and crisp, while the casing makes it easy to hold and use for browsing the web, watching videos or just using many of the apps available from Google Play.

The tablet is powered by a 1GHz dual-core Nvidia Tegra 2 processor and is super-slick. The only time we did see a lag was when first reviewing the device and rotating the screen, but this seems to have been rectified with an update.

The cameras on the Galaxy Tab 8.9 really aren't worth using, although we don't really understand the inclusion of cameras on tablets anyway.

The final point of note is the Galaxy Tab 8.9 features a hefty 6100mAH battery that promises eight to 10 hours of constant use - including video. It's pretty good, especially as we're yet to see more impressive battery life on such large-screened devices.

The Samsung Galaxy Tab 8.9 sits in the middle of the Galaxy Tab range and, at the end of the day, which you choose comes down to personal preference on size. Upgradeable to Android Jelly Bean, the Tab 8.9 is perfect if you want a tablet that you can hold with one hand, but is also comfortable for watching video content on.

ANNOUNCED
March 2011

CONTRACT PRICE
N/A, from £400 SIM free

PREPAY PRICE
N/A

SIZE
230.9 x 157.8 x 8.6mm

WEIGHT
453g

SCREEN SIZE
8.9-inches

STORAGE
16/32/64GB

CAMERA
3.15-megapixels

PROCESSOR
1GHz dual-core Nvidia Tegra 2

BATTERY LIFE
72 hours standby
9 hours talktime

ANDROID VERSION
Ice Cream Sandwich, version 4.0.3
upgradeable to version 4.1

Samsung Galaxy Tab 10.1

The Galaxy Tab 10.1 has a larger screen and is faster and sexier than the original Galaxy Tab. It also comes pre-loaded with a true tablet OS – Honeycomb, to be precise.

Its 1280×800 pixel resolution 10.1-inch display offers amazing brightness, bold colours and wide viewing angles, making it without a shadow of a doubt the best screen on a tablet device.

Samsung has had to remove some features that many customers may consider to be vital, including a memory card slot, which means you can't add more storage via SD cards. The tablet comes in 16GB and 32GB variants, so if you intend to store masses of content onto the device, make sure you go with the higher-capacity option.

The Galaxy Tab 10.1's 7000mAh battery offers around 10 hours of moderate use, although that figure will come down if you're constantly watching HD movies.

The stunning screen and sexy design put the Galaxy Tab on even terms with the iPad from a technical and cosmetic standpoint, but the lack of developer support and the omission of Android hallmarks such as expandable memory and USB ports is disappointing.

If you're after an Android tablet and are not concerned with adding more memory or hooking up USB peripherals, then this is probably your best bet. It's the first Android tablet which looks as good as it performs, and that screen is simply to die for.

ANNOUNCED
March 2011

CONTRACT PRICE
N/A, from £400 SIM free

PREPAY PRICE
N/A

SIZE
256.7 x 175.3 x 8.6mm

WEIGHT
565g

SCREEN SIZE
10.1-inches

STORAGE
16/32GB

CAMERA
3-megapixels

PROCESSOR
Dual-core 1GHz Cortex-A9

BATTERY LIFE
1840 hours standby
9 hours talktime

ANDROID VERSION
Honeycomb, version 3.0 (Honeycomb), upgradeable to Ice Cream Sandwich version 4.0

Samsung Galaxy Tab 2 7.0

The Samsung Galaxy Tab 2 series is a follow up to the original Galaxy Tab range but, with an updated operating system, it offers more features.

The Samsung Galaxy Tab 2 7.0, like the Galaxy Tab and Galaxy Tab 7.0 Plus, slides into a bag or pocket in an almost unnoticeable way.

The Tab 2 7.0 can be held with just one hand and the screen provides the perfect resolution and size for reading books or browsing the web.

You won't get as much of a full-screen video experience as the Tab 2 10.1, but surely if you wanted to watch the latest blockbuster, you'd purchase the 10-inch version?

With a 1GHz processor, it's not going to win any awards for speed, but the UI does run fluidly, especially if you install Android Jelly Bean, which has now become available on the tablet.

On the back of the Tab 2 7.0 is a 3-megapixel camera, which isn't up to the standard of smartphones. That said, it's a little awkward to take a photo with a 7-inch device anyway.

The Samsung Galaxy Tab 2 7.0 is an OK tablet for less than £300, but the Galaxy Nexus 7 trumps it in almost every way, including price.

ANNOUNCED
February 2012

CONTRACT PRICE
N/A, from £250 SIM free

PREPAY PRICE
N/A

SIZE
193.7 x 122.4 x 10.5mm

WEIGHT
345g

SCREEN SIZE
7-inches

STORAGE
8/16/32GB

CAMERA
3.15-megapixels

PROCESSOR
Dual-core 1GHz

BATTERY LIFE
1080 hours standby
20 hours talktime

ANDROID VERSION
Ice Cream Sandwich, version 4.0.3
upgradeable to version 4.1

Samsung Galaxy Tab 2 10.1

The Samsung Galaxy Tab 2 7.0's bigger brother, the Galaxy Tab 2 10.1, is the same size as the iPad, but with a lower price tag and lower spec to match.

Design-wise, the Galaxy Tab 2 10.1 matches the Galaxy Tab 2 7.0 but, with a larger, 10.1-inch screen, it's quite a bit heavier.

The Tab 2 10.1's screen is ultra-reflective, which isn't particularly great if you're heading out into bright sunlight.

Both cameras on the tablet are pretty poor quality, without flash, auto focus or any manual options that lower-priced devices offer. There also isn't a Wi-Fi option, which means you're limited to buying a MiFi or relying on Wi-Fi hotspots.

Video playback is probably the finest point of the Galaxy Tab 2 10.1, but that's due to its large screen - the perfect size for mobile movie watching.

Browsing is also good, but again, that's likely due to the size rather than performance.

The Galaxy Tab 2 10.1 is a pretty average tablet when compared to many on the market around the same price point. Although it's great for watching movies on the move, there are plenty of other tablets on the market that offer more - we would even recommend the Galaxy Note 10.1 over this.

ANNOUNCED
February 2012

CONTRACT PRICE
N/A, from £325 SIM free

PREPAY PRICE
N/A

SIZE
256.6 x 175.3 x 9.7mm

WEIGHT
588g

SCREEN SIZE
10.1-inches

STORAGE
16/32GB

CAMERA
3.15-megapixels

PROCESSOR
Dual-core 1GHz Cortex-A9

BATTERY LIFE
2000 hours standby
10 hours talktime

ANDROID VERSION
Ice Cream Sandwich, version 4.0.3
upgradeable to version 4.1

Samsung Galaxy S

ANNOUNCED
March 2010

CONTRACT PRICE
No longer available

PREPAY PRICE
No longer available

SIZE
122.4 x 64.2 x 9.9mm

WEIGHT
119g

SCREEN SIZE
4-inches

STORAGE
8/16GB

CAMERA
5-megapixels

PROCESSOR
1GHz Cortex-A8

BATTERY LIFE
576 hours standby
6.5 hours talktime

ANDROID VERSION
Eclair, version 2.1,
upgradeable to version 2.3

Samsung Galaxy Y

ANNOUNCED
August 2011

CONTRACT PRICE
Free from £7.50 a month

PREPAY PRICE
£50

SIZE
104 x 58 x 11.5mm

WEIGHT
97.5g

SCREEN SIZE
3-inches

STORAGE
180MB

CAMERA
2-megapixels

PROCESSOR
830MHz ARMv6

BATTERY LIFE
540 hours standby
6 hours talktime

ANDROID VERSION
Gingerbread, version 2.3.5

Samsung Galaxy Mini

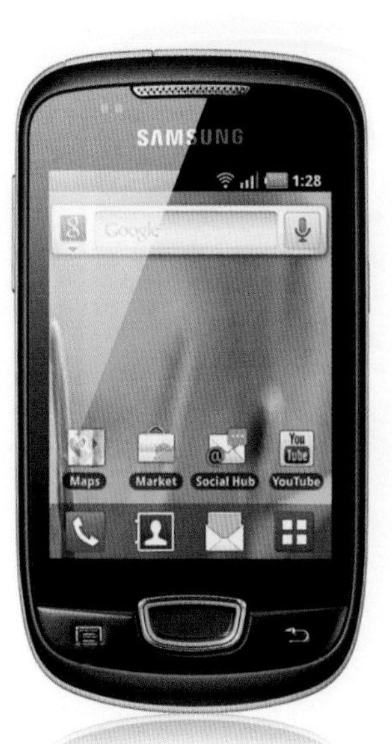

ANNOUNCED
January 2011

CONTRACT PRICE
Free from £7 per month

PREPAY PRICE
£70

SIZE
110.4 x 60.8 x 12.1mm

WEIGHT
105g

SCREEN SIZE
3.14-inches

STORAGE
160MB

CAMERA
3.15-megapixels

PROCESSOR
600MHz ARMv6

BATTERY LIFE
570 hours standby
9.5 hours talktime

ANDROID VERSION
Froyo version 2.0.3,
upgradeable to version 2.3

Samsung Galaxy Pro

ANNOUNCED
April 2011

CONTRACT PRICE
N/A, from £190 SIM free

PREPAY PRICE
N/A

SIZE
108.6 x 66.7 x 10.7mm

WEIGHT
103.4g

SCREEN SIZE
2.8-inches

STORAGE
160MB

CAMERA
3.15-megapixels

PROCESSOR
800MHz ARMv6

BATTERY LIFE
430 hours standby
6 hours talktime

ANDROID VERSION
Froyo, version 2.2.2

Samsung Galaxy Ace

ANNOUNCED
January 2011

CONTRACT PRICE
N/A, from £150 SIM free

PREPAY PRICE
N/A

SIZE
112.4 x 59.9 x 11.5mm

WEIGHT
113g

SCREEN SIZE
3.5-inches

STORAGE
158MB

CAMERA
5-megapixels

PROCESSOR
800MHz ARM 11

BATTERY LIFE
420 hours standby
6.5 hours talktime

ANDROID VERSION
Gingerbread, version 2.3

Samsung Galaxy Europa

ANNOUNCED
June 2010

CONTRACT PRICE
N/A, from £130 SIM free

PREPAY PRICE
£65

SIZE
108 x 56 x 12.3mm

WEIGHT
102g

SCREEN SIZE
2.8-inches

STORAGE
140MB

CAMERA
2-megapixels

PROCESSOR
600MHz

BATTERY LIFE
375 hours standby
6.5 hours talktime

ANDROID VERSION
Éclair, version 2.1,
upgradeable to Froyo version 2.2

Samsung Galaxy S Plus

ANNOUNCED
April 2011

CONTRACT PRICE
N/A, from £280 SIM free

PREPAY PRICE
N/A

SIZE
122.4 x 64.2 x 9.9mm

WEIGHT
119g

SCREEN SIZE
4-inches

STORAGE
8/16GB

CAMERA
5-megapixels

PROCESSOR
1.4GHz Scorpion

BATTERY LIFE
430 hours standby
7.5 hours talktime

ANDROID VERSION
Gingerbread, version 2.3

Samsung Galaxy Apollo

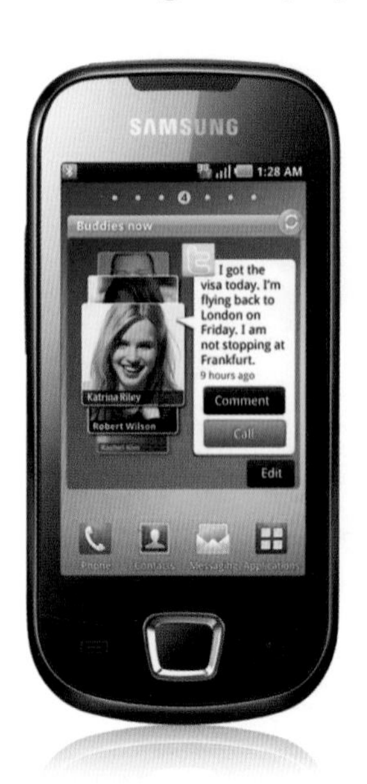

ANNOUNCED
June 2010

CONTRACT PRICE
N/A

PREPAY PRICE
£95

SIZE
113.5 x 55 x 12.6mm

WEIGHT
113g

SCREEN SIZE
3.2-inches

STORAGE
512MB

CAMERA
3.15-megapixels

PROCESSOR
667MHz

BATTERY LIFE
480 hours standby
7 hours talktime

ANDROID VERSION
Éclair, version 2.1,
upgradeable to version 2.2

Samsung Galaxy Fit

ANNOUNCED
January 2011

CONTRACT PRICE
Free from £10.50 per month

PREPAY PRICE
£85

SIZE
110.2 x 61.2 x 12.6mm

WEIGHT
108g

SCREEN SIZE
3.5-inches

STORAGE
158MB

CAMERA
5-megapixels

PROCESSOR
600MHz

BATTERY LIFE
421 hours standby
6.5 hours talktime

ANDROID VERSION
Froyo version 202, upgradeable to Gingerbread version 2.3

Samsung Galaxy W

ANNOUNCED
August 2011

CONTRACT PRICE
N/A, £210 SIM free

PREPAY PRICE
N/A

SIZE
115.5 x 59.8 x 11.5mm

WEIGHT
114.7g

SCREEN SIZE
3.7-inches

STORAGE
1.7GB

CAMERA
5-megapixels

PROCESSOR
1.4GHz Scorpion

BATTERY LIFE
420 hours standby
8 hours talktime

ANDROID VERSION
Gingerbread, version 2.3.5

Samsung Galaxy Tab 7.0 Plus

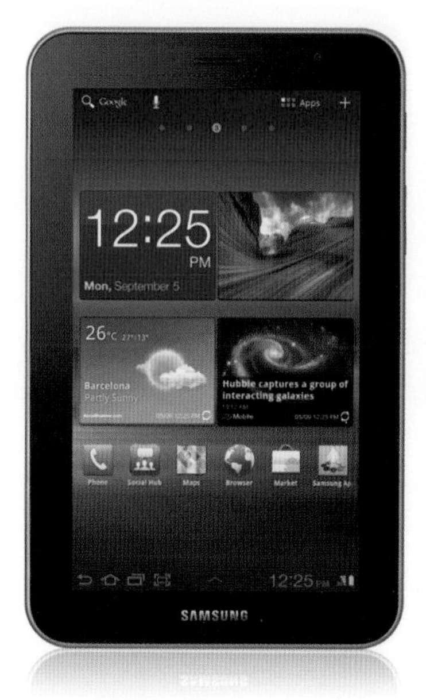

ANNOUNCED
October 2011

CONTRACT PRICE
N/A, from £400 SIM free

PREPAY PRICE
N/A

SIZE
193.7 x 122.4 x 9.99mm

WEIGHT
345g

SCREEN SIZE
7-inches

STORAGE
16/32GB

CAMERA
3.15-megapixels

PROCESSOR
Dual-core 1.2GHz

BATTERY LIFE
1000 hours standby
20 hours talktime

ANDROID VERSION
Honeycomb version 3.1, upgradeable to version 4.1

Samsung Galaxy Y Pro

ANNOUNCED
August 2011

CONTRACT PRICE
N/A, from £130 SIM free

PREPAY PRICE
N/A

SIZE
10.8 x 63.5 x 11.5mm

WEIGHT
108.6g

SCREEN SIZE
2.6-inches

STORAGE
160MB

CAMERA
3.15-megapixels

PROCESSOR
832MHz

BATTERY LIFE
500 hours standby
6 hours talktime

ANDROID VERSION
Gingerbread, version 2.3

Samsung Galaxy Xcover

ANNOUNCED
August 2011

CONTRACT PRICE
Free from £10.50 per month

PREPAY PRICE
N/A

SIZE
121.5 x 65.9 x 12mm

WEIGHT
100g

SCREEN SIZE
3.65-inches

STORAGE
150MB

CAMERA
3.15-megapixels

PROCESSOR
800MHz Marvell MG2

BATTERY LIFE
640 hours standby
11 hours talktime

ANDROID VERSION
Gingerbread, version 2.3

Samsung Galaxy R

ANNOUNCED
June 2011

CONTRACT PRICE
N/A, from £699 SIM free

PREPAY PRICE
N/A

SIZE
125 x 66 x 9.5mm

WEIGHT
135g

SCREEN SIZE
4.2-inches

STORAGE
8GB

CAMERA
5-megapixels

PROCESSOR
Dual-core 1.2GHz Cortex-A9

BATTERY LIFE
550 hours standby
9 hours talktime

ANDROID VERSION
Gingerbread version 2.3, upgradeable to version 4.0

Samsung Galaxy Gio

ANNOUNCED
January 2011

CONTRACT PRICE
N/A, from £150 SIM free

PREPAY PRICE
N/A

SIZE
110.5 x 57.5 x 12.2mm

WEIGHT
102g

SCREEN SIZE
3.2-inches

STORAGE
158MB

CAMERA
3.15-megapixels

PROCESSOR
800MHz

BATTERY LIFE
460 hours standby
6.5 hours talktime

ANDROID VERSION
Froyo version 2.2, upgradeable to version 2.3

Samsung Galaxy Ace Plus

ANNOUNCED
January 2012

CONTRACT PRICE
Free from £13.50 per month

PREPAY PRICE
N/A

SIZE
114.5 x 62.5 x 11.2mm

WEIGHT
115g

SCREEN SIZE
3.65-inches

STORAGE
3GB

CAMERA
5-megapixels

PROCESSOR
1GHz Cortex-A5

BATTERY LIFE
420 hours standby
7 hours talktime

ANDROID VERSION
Gingerbread version 2.3, upgradeable to version 4.1

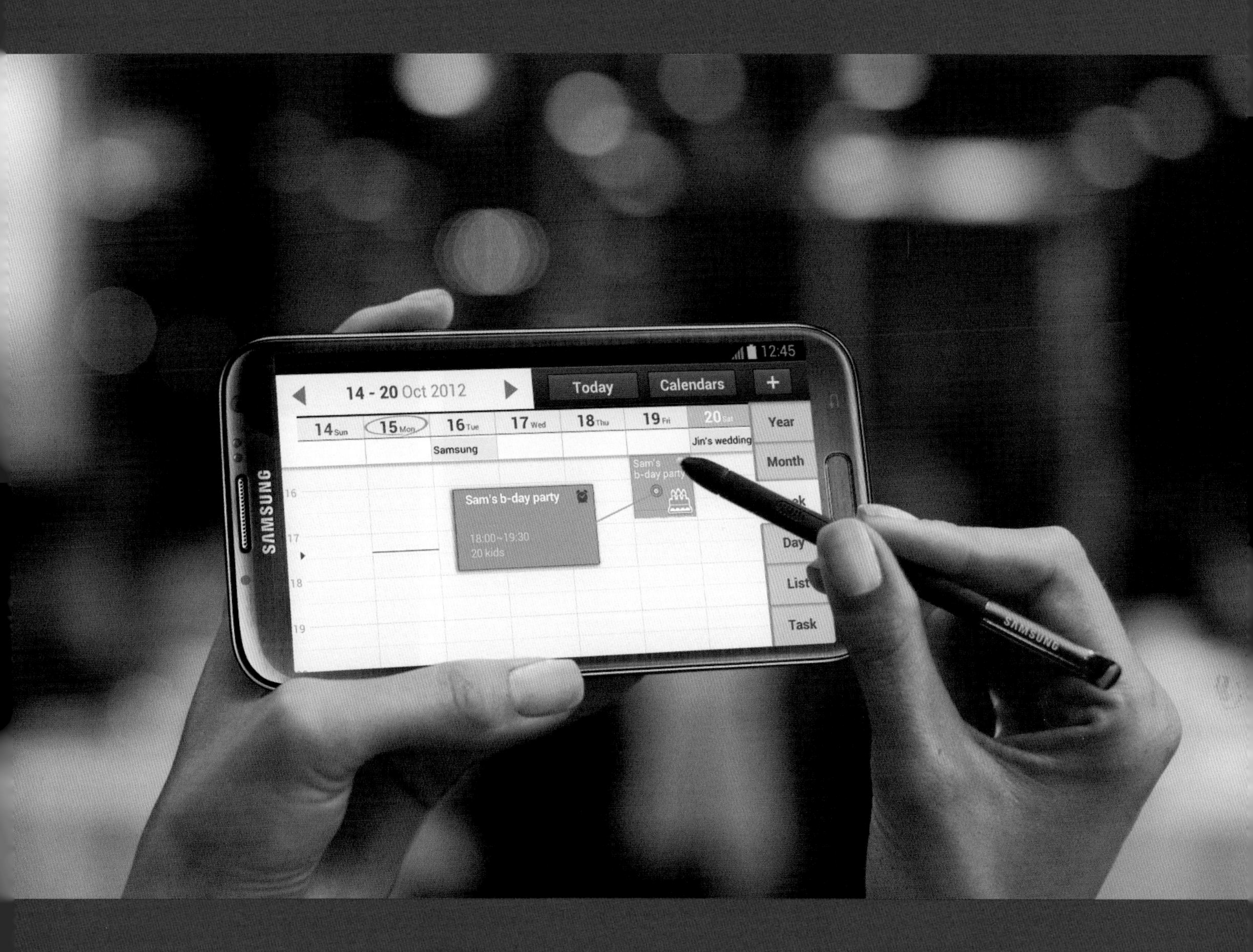

Chapter 3

Setting up your Galaxy

Samsung set up manager

If the Samsung Galaxy is your first Android smartphone, you'll find that, thanks to the Android set-up manager, it's a doddle to get everything ship-shape on your device, including setting up the time, language, Wi-Fi, your Google account and more.

When you turn your Galaxy device on for the first time, you'll be taken through the steps to set up your device the way you want it.

You can change many of these settings from the main settings menu. To access this at any time, just open the apps tray and swipe your way to the screen where you'll find 'Settings'.

Please note: Although the process for setting up your Samsung Galaxy is the same whatever device you have and Android version you're using, the way it is presented on the screen may differ.

Top Secret Tip

You can block unwanted phone calls on your Samsung device very easily, so only your contacts can get through to you. Go to Settings > Blocking mode > click Enable and then scroll to the bottom of the screen. Choose Allowed contacts and select who you want to allow to call you.

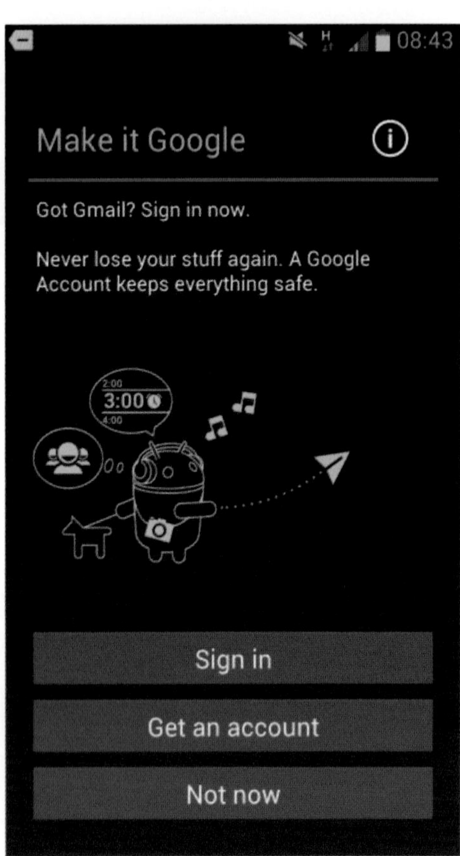

Setting the date, time and language

- First, you'll need to choose your language and the date and time. Check those displayed are correct and tap 'Next' (your phone will automatically use your network to set the date and time).

Setting up your Samsung account

- Your Samsung Galaxy will now ask if you have a Samsung account (the Galaxy Nexus will skip this step). You can sign in if you have one, set up a new account or skip the step altogether.

Setting up your Google account

- You'll be asked if you have a Google account or not. This will set up your email for you as well as registering your email account for services like Google Play, which is the Android application, music and video store.

- If you haven't already set one up, you can do so by pressing 'No'. If you do have a Google account, enter your username and password when requested.

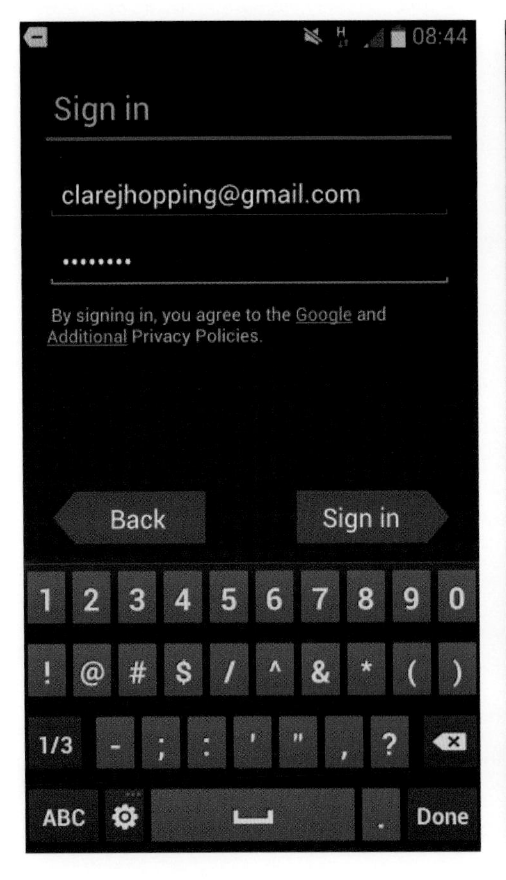

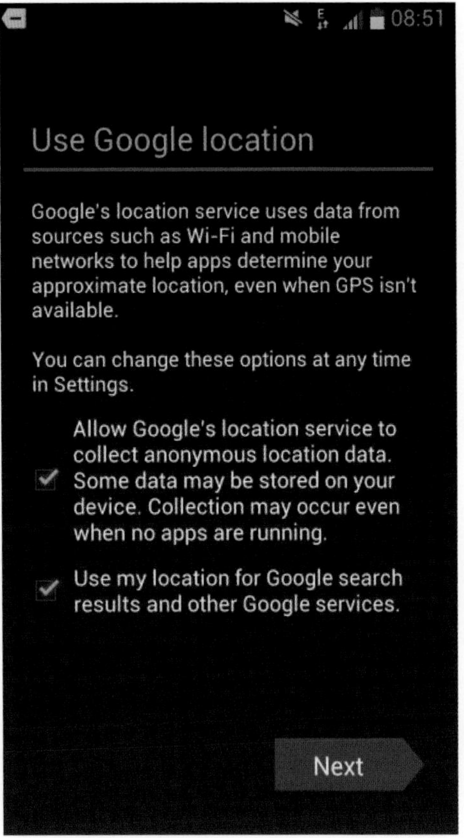

Terms and conditions

- Accept the Google terms and conditions, privacy policy and Google Play terms of service when requested, all of which can be read via the links provided. You will need to accept these to use your phone.

- You will now be signed into your Google account, but it may take a little time depending on your internet connection.

Backup and restore

- Your phone will now ask if you'd like to back up and restore your phone. If you've used Android before, it will restore your phone to the last used settings. It may take some time though depending on what you had installed.

Use Google location

- Here, you can opt whether you'd like Google to collect and store your location data for Wi-Fi hotspots and mobile networks. It'll stay stored on your device and could be used for things like remembering Wi-Fi network connection details.

- You can also opt in to your Samsung phone using your location in Google search results and other Google services. Allowing this will provide better, more relevant search results for you.

Providing your name

- Adding your name on the 'This phone belongs to...' screen will mean some apps will use your name when greeting you. It's not essential, but adds that little personal touch.

Dropbox

- Dropbox is a cloud storage service that can store documents, photos, videos and any other files. If you set the service up on your computer too, you can access your files wherever you are. You can also access the service via a browser.

- After you've set up an account or entered your existing details, you can choose whether you want all your photos and videos automatically saved to Dropbox.

Homescreen and widgets

The homescreen on your Samsung Galaxy device is completely customisable and you can even add and delete extra screens to change the number of apps at your fingertips.

Adding and deleting homescreens

- To add a new homescreen, long press and hold any existing homescreen. Choose the top option and then select 'Page.' You'll be taken to the homescreen overview screen. Just tap on the screen with a '+' displayed to add a new screen.

- If this option isn't offered (on newer versions of Android), press the menu key from the homescreen (the left key below the screen) and select 'Edit page' to get to the homescreen overview screen.

- To delete a homescreen, follow the same process as above, but when you get to the homescreen overview page, press and hold the page you want to delete then drag it to the recycle bin at the bottom of the screen.

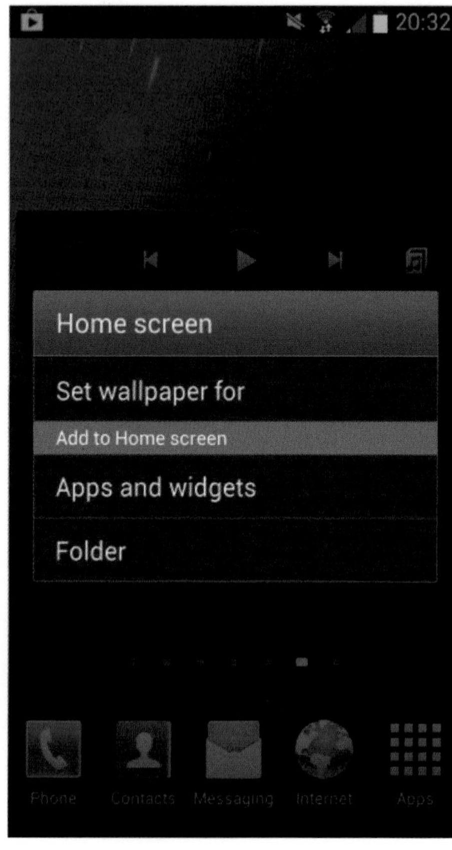

Adding a wallpaper

- To add a wallpaper to your homescreen, lock screen or both, press and hold a homescreen and select Wallpaper > Homescreen/lock screen/homescreen and lock screen.

- Select the wallpaper you want to change and select where to get the picture from. Your Galaxy phone has a number of preinstalled wallpapers or you can use one of your pictures from the gallery.

- The homescreen supports active wallpapers too.

- Choose a picture or wallpaper from the relevant album. If you're choosing one of your own pictures, you'll be invited to crop your picture. Tap 'Done' and your wallpaper will be set.

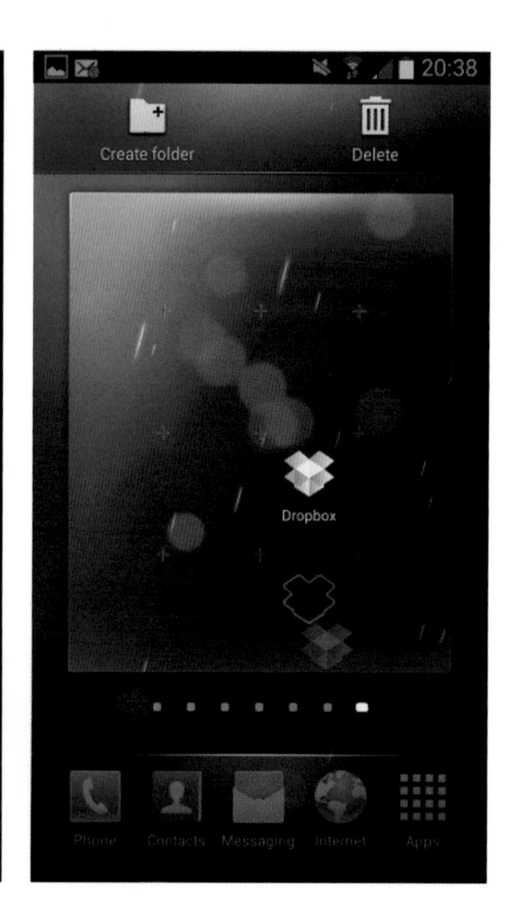

Adding widgets and apps to the homescreen

- To add a widget to your Samsung's homescreen, press and hold any homescreen, then tap 'Add to homescreen.'

- Next, choose apps or widgets and press and hold the app or widget you want to add, and move it to where you want it, sliding along to change homescreen. You can also add bookmarks to your favourite websites and shortcuts to apps.

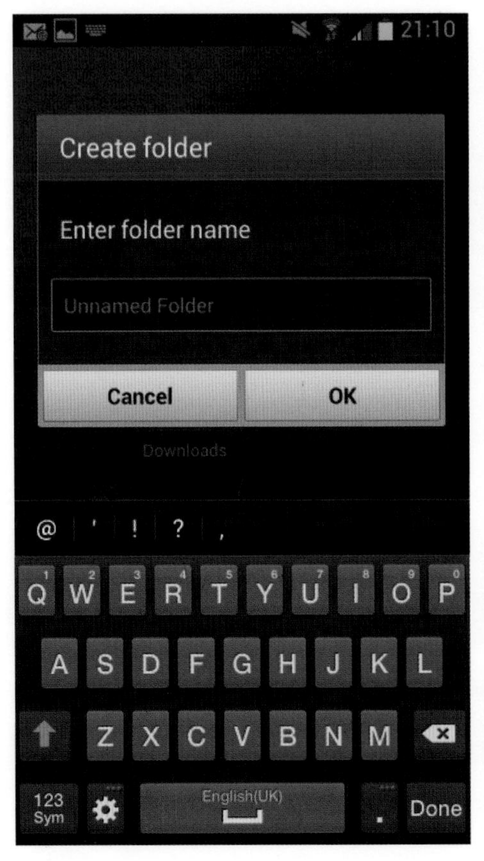

Adding folders

- You can organise your apps into folders to make things easier to find from the homescreen. To do so, long press the homescreen and select 'Add to homescreen'. Choose the folder and name it something memorable or descriptive and drag and drop the apps you want to put in the folder.

Top Secret Tip

A little low on free minutes or credit? You can make free calls on your Samsung Galaxy device by downloading and installing Skype, an application that allows you to call people over Wi-Fi. Your contacts will have to be on Skype too, but it's worth spreading the word. That way, you can all save money!

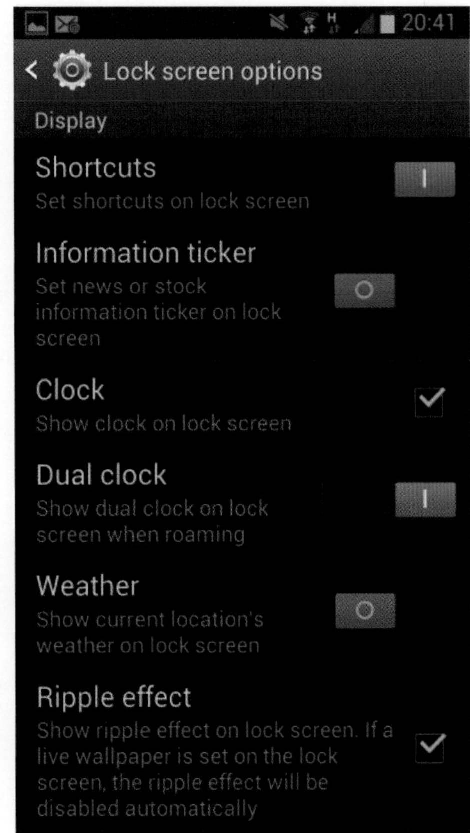

Adding apps to lock screen

- Your Samsung's Touchwiz interface allows you to add shortcuts to your homescreen so you can launch them without unlocking your phone. To do this, navigate to and open the 'Settings' app.

- Now scroll down the settings menu and tap 'Security' then 'Lock screen options.'

Note: The Lock screen menu may just sit it the Personal folder, alongside Security.

- Now confirm that the shortcut button is turned on and then tap 'Shortcuts.'

- Now you will be presented with four icons. Drag those that you want to remove from the lock screen to the trash and use the '+' symbol to add new app shortcuts.

Top five launcher apps for Android

- Launcher Pro
- Apex Launcher
- Go Launcher EX
- Nova Launcher
- ADW Launcher EX

Contacts

Your contacts book is where all of your phone numbers, email addresses and information about the people you communicate with live. When you first turn your phone on, you'll probably find it's empty, so just follow these tips to start topping it up.

Synching contacts
If you haven't already added a Google account, you'll be asked again to do it here. It's a good idea if you already have all your contacts backed up to Google because it will import them instantly. Just enter your Gmail details and all your contacts will be added to your contacts list, including email addresses, phone numbers and any other details you have stored on Google.

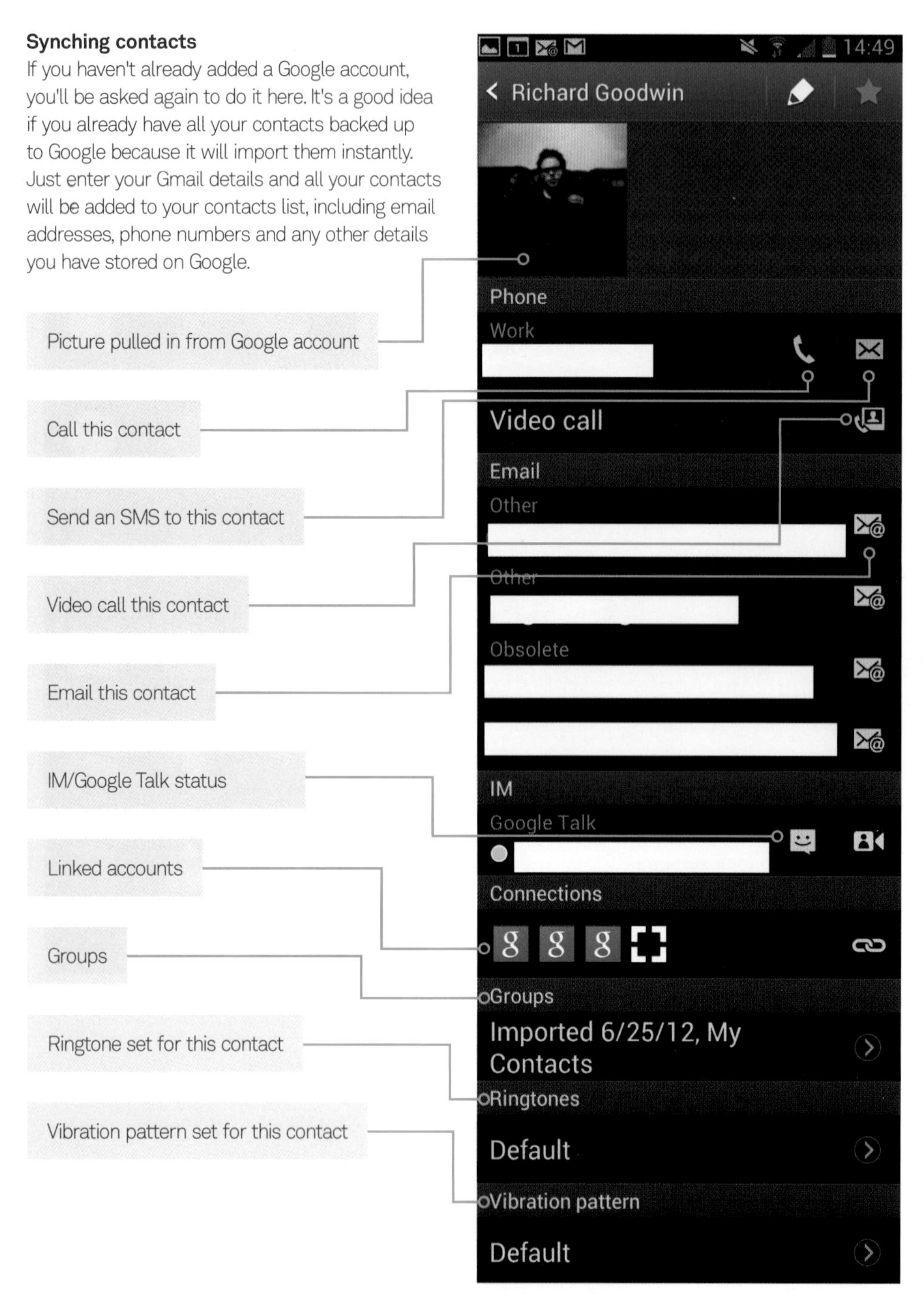

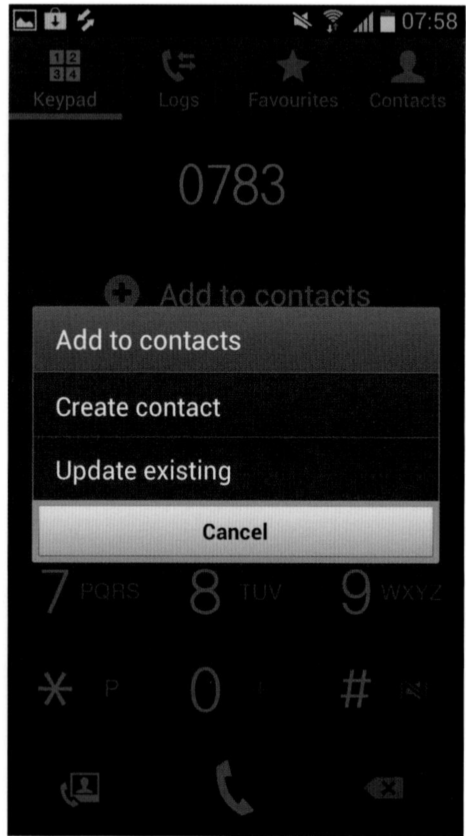

Manually adding contacts

- To add contacts manually, you can start right from the phone screen. Just type in a contact's number and an 'Add contact' box will pop up. Tap it and then either select 'Update existing' to link it to an existing contact (just choose the contact from your existing list) or 'Create contact.' Choose where you want to save it (we recommend Google to have a back up) and then enter the details. Tap 'Save'.
- You can also add a contact by navigating to 'Contacts' and tapping the '+' icon next to the search bar.

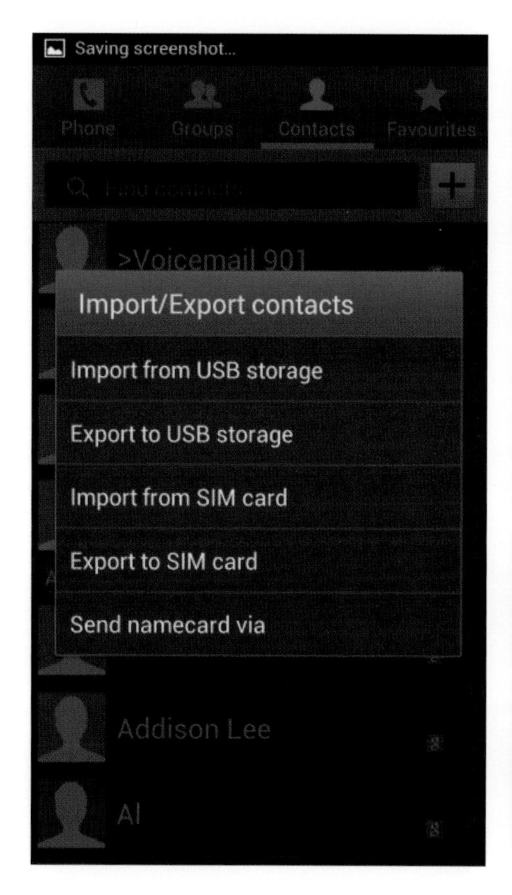

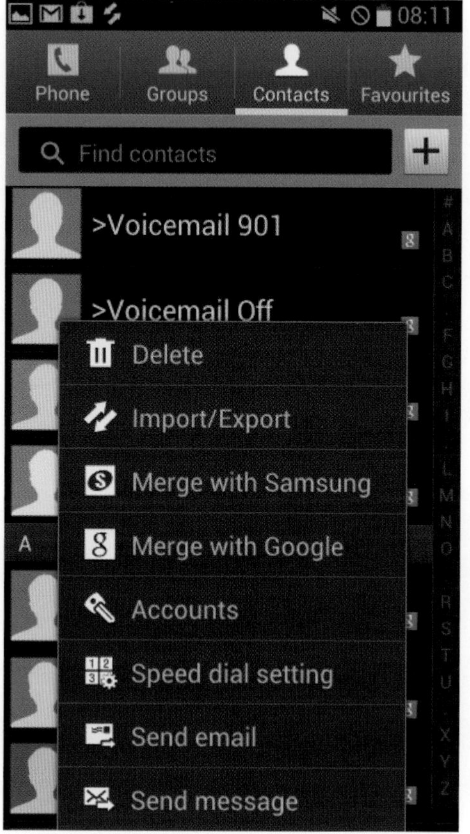

Importing contacts

➲ If you have contacts saved on your SIM card and are just transferring them across to your new Galaxy, open up the 'Contacts' application and tap the 'Menu' icon. This will vary according to which device you're using, but it's normally the left soft key or touchscreen button. Now, select 'Import/export' and choose I'mport from SIM card.' You can choose which account you'd like it linked to or just save to your phone.

Exporting contacts

➲ Follow the instructions above, but select 'Export to SIM card'. You can select one contact or all and then click 'Done' and they'll be transferred.

Removing contacts

➲ To delete a contact or number of contacts, tap the menu key from inside the 'Contacts' app and select 'Delete'. Now. choose which contacts you want to delete and tap 'Done'.

Sending a contact

➲ To send a contact via vCard (the standard way of sending contacts across any mobile platform or computer), choose 'Import/export contacts' as above and then choose 'Send name card via'. Select the contact you want to send, hit 'Done' and then choose how you'd like to send the contact.

Creating a group

➲ You can set up groups in your contacts to communicate with certain friends or contacts at the same time. To do this, navigate to the 'Groups' tab from the 'Contacts' app and press the menu button. Select 'New,' name your group, add a ringtone if you wish, then start adding your contacts. You can, of course, use any predefined groups too.

Adding contacts to your Favourites

➲ You can easily add contacts to your favourites on your Samsung Galaxy so you have access to them in just a couple of taps.

➲ To set this up, head to your contacts list and tap the 'Favourites' tab. Now press the menu button under the screen and 'Add to favourites'. Select the contact(s) you want to add and hit 'Done'.

Calling

Calling is a pretty basic, but necessary, function on any phone, and Samsung Galaxy devices are no different. Here, we show you some of the basic functions of the calling screen.

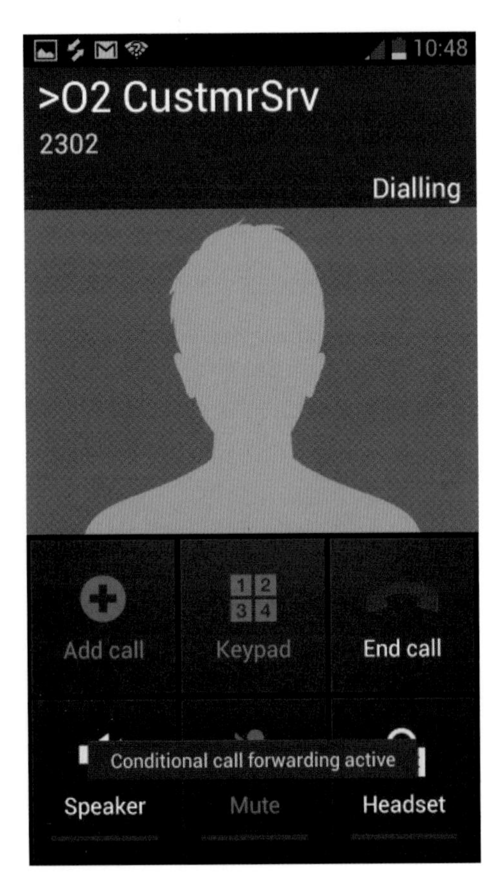

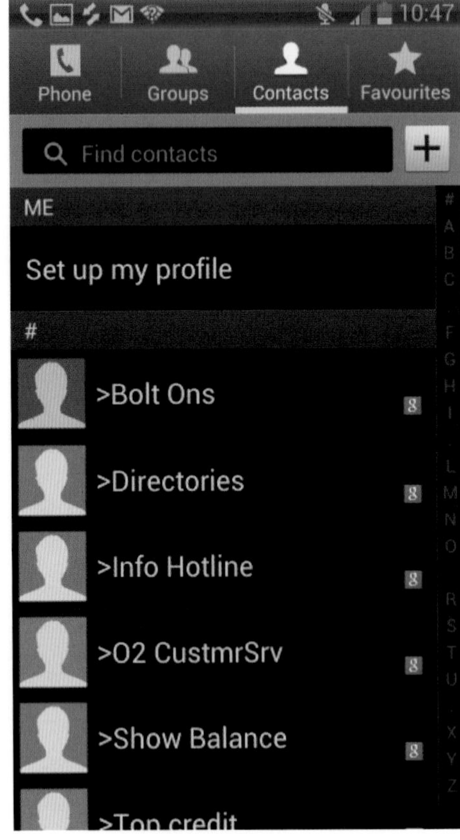

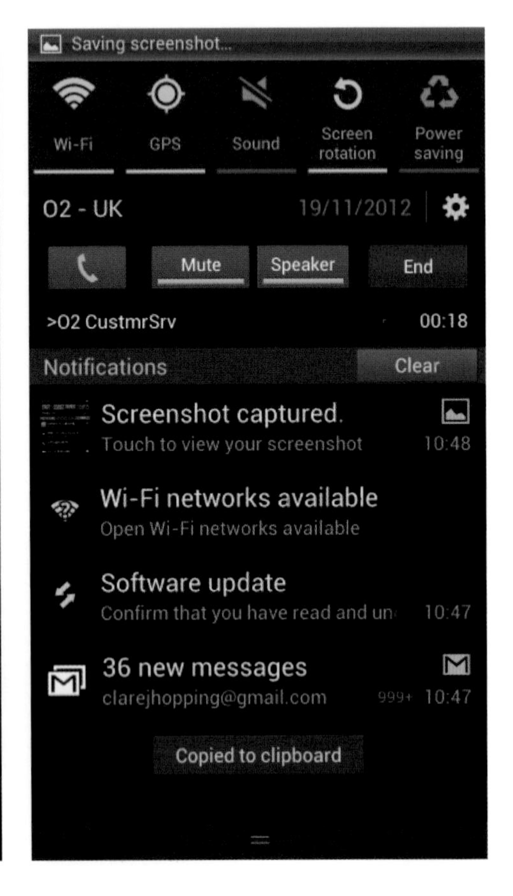

Phoning from contacts

- Head to 'Contacts', choose the person you want to call and either swipe left to right on the name to call or tap to open the contact and then the phone number to start a call.

- Your third option for making a call is via S Voice, Samsung's voice recognition feature. You can find out more about this on page 110.

Top Secret Tip

You can instantly silence some Samsung Galaxy smartphones just by turning them over. This works on all Samsung devices with S-services enabled, such as the Samsung Galaxy S III. Just go to Settings > Motion > Motion activation > Turn over to mute/pause to activate.

Conference calling

- To make a conference call, head to the contacts screen or dialler and enter the number you want to call. Tap the green phone icon to make the call and put the first call on hold (see below for how to do this).

- While on the first call, you can dial new contacts in by tapping on 'Add call'. You'll be taken to the contacts app where you can search for a contact to add into the call, dial a new number or add a favourite or group.

- Make the call and then head to the call status screen where you will see that one call is on hold and the other is active. Now tap 'Merge' to unite the two calls.

Putting a call on hold

- To put a call on hold, tap the pause icon at the bottom of the caller screen. The phone call will now display as on hold.

Activating the speakerphone

- Activating the speakerphone is easy on your Samsung Galaxy. You just need to tap the speaker icon at the bottom of the call screen. You can also pull down the status bar and tap 'Speaker' to go into speaker mode or mute if you don't want the person on the other end to hear you.

Messaging

You'll find everything you need to get started for SMS in the Messaging folder which is represented by a yellow and white envelope icon on TouchWiz-enabled devices or a green speech bubble icon on the Galaxy Nexus.

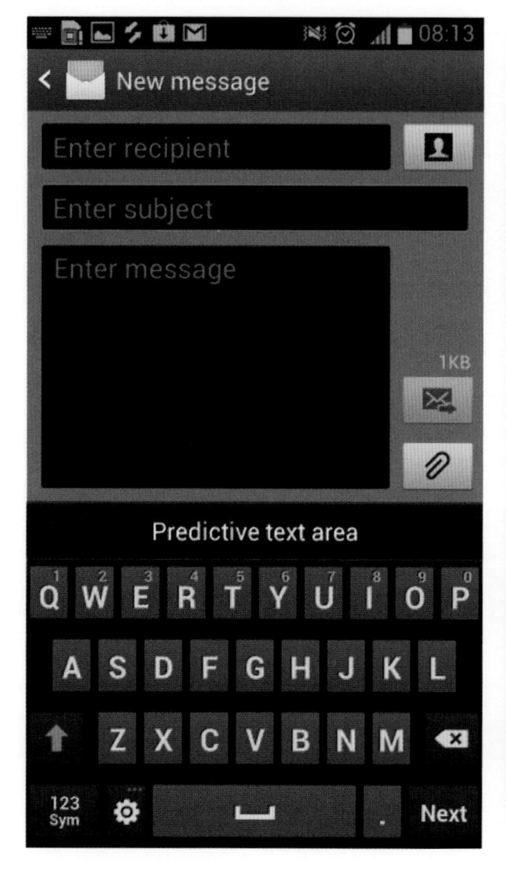

Composing texts

- To compose a message, tap 'Messaging' and then the pen icon in the top right of the screen. Enter the recipient of the message by tying the first characters of their name or phone number in the box.

- Now type your message and select the envelope icon to send the message.

- You can also add a subject by pressing the menu button and selecting 'Add subject'. This will create an additional field where you can add a subject to your message.

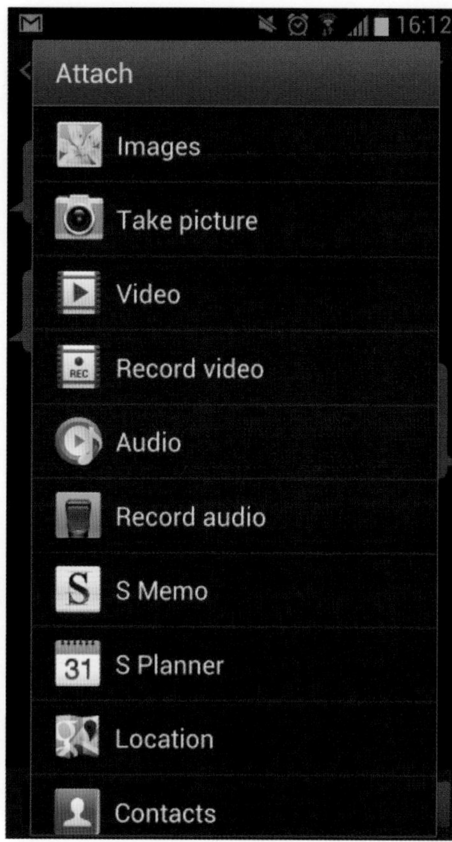

Adding attachments

- After composing your message as above, tap the paperclip icon to add an attachment. You can add everything, from a picture to an audio clip, location, memo, contact and more. Just select the relevant media, choose the file and select the envelope icon to send.

Group texting

- To send a text to a group rather than an individual, compose a message and select the contacts icon next to the recipient. Tap 'Groups,' select the group and then the contacts from that group you want to send the text to. Tap 'Done' and the contacts from that group will be added to the recipient list.

- Then simply create the message and send.

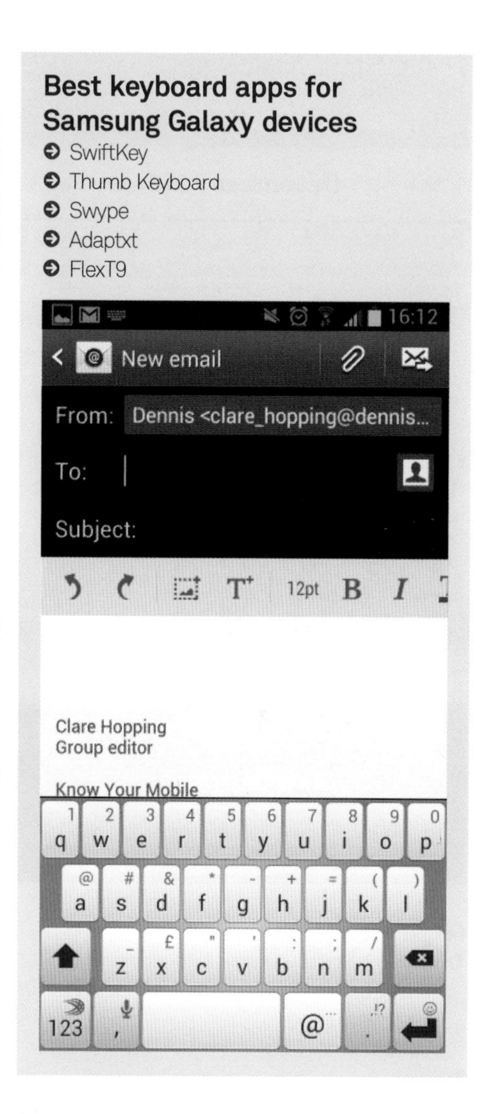

Best keyboard apps for Samsung Galaxy devices

- SwiftKey
- Thumb Keyboard
- Swype
- Adaptxt
- FlexT9

Secure messages

Android doesn't feature the ability to secure your text messages or hide them from prying eyes, but there are loads of apps available that will allow you to password-protect your messages so colleagues, friends or family can't see them. Here are our favourites:

- Secure SMS
- TextSecure
- Indigo Secure SMS

Calendar (S Planner)

The calendar is called the S Planner on your Samsung Galaxy phone and it allows you to merge calendars with any of your email accounts, Facebook, or manually.

Forget about your Filofax

- You'll get alerts whenever an appointment is coming up so you can pretty much ditch your paper diary forever.
- When you set up your email or Facebook account on your Samsung Galaxy device, it will ask you what you want to sync from your account. If you choose to synchronise your calendar, all entries will appear in your handset's calendar app.

Changing the calendar view

- When you open up the S Planner, by default, you'll be able to see the month calendar. To access alternative views, tap the left-facing arrow in the top-right of the screen.
- You'll now see a number of tabs down the right side of the screen, including Year, Month, Week, Day, Agenda and Task. Tap any of these to see the period in full screen mode.

Top Secret Tip

If your contacts are getting a little out of hand, with one entry linked to your Google, another to work and a third via Facebook, link them all by heading to Contacts > the contact you want to link > chain icon > Join other contacts > Select contacts you want to link.

Choosing which calendars to sync

- When you open the S Planner app, you'll see all your merged calendar entries from all your accounts. If you want to minimise the number of calendars that sync with your device, tap on the calendars tab at the top of the S Planner.
- Tap on the calendars to add them or remove them from your calendar.
- By default, all those associated with your email and Facebook accounts are synced, but you can also add extras, such as UK holidays and Phases of the moon.
- Once you've selected the calendars you wish to sync, tap 'Done' and you'll be taken back to the calendar view where different calendars will be colour coded.

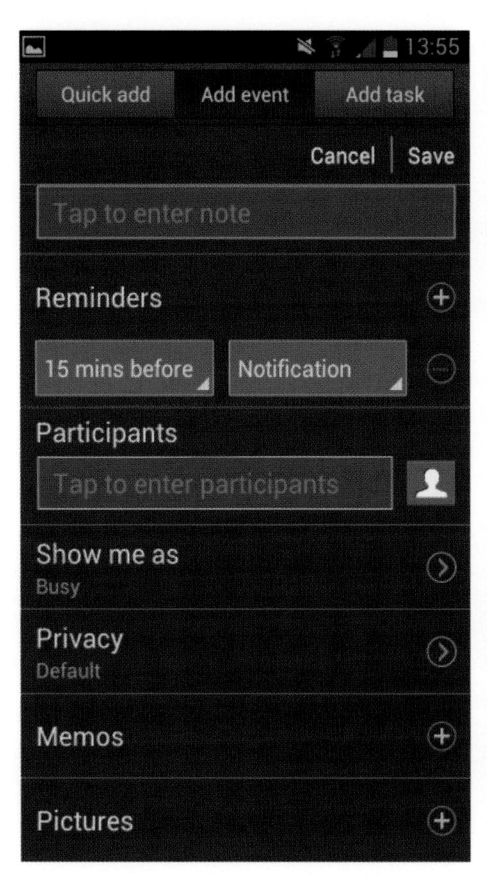

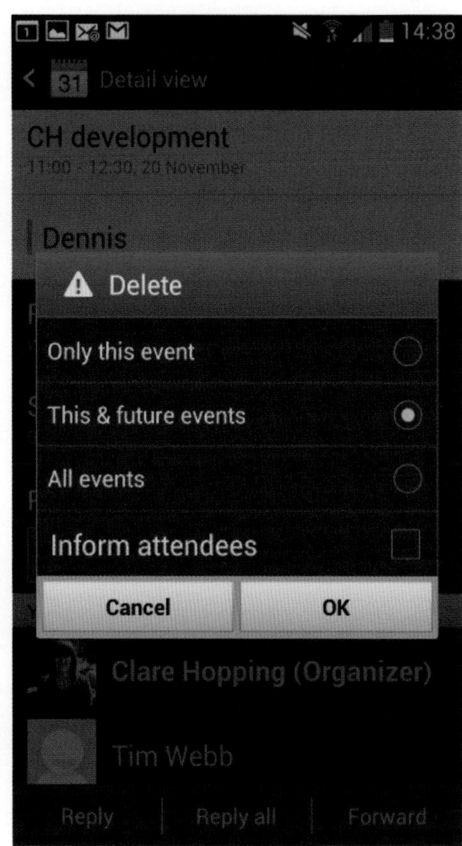

Best calendar apps

- CalenGoo
- Touch Calendar
- Simple Calendar Widget
- MyCalendar Free
- Business Calendar Free

Adding an entry

- If you want to add a calendar entry manually to your device, open up the calendar widget and tap the '+' at the top of the screen.

- You can opt to add an entry using Quick add – just write in text your event, for example 'Team lunch tomorrow at 12PM', followed by 'Save'. The device will automatically decipher the text and add it to the calendar.

- For a little more information, select 'Add event'. Now enter a title and more detailed information. You can also choose to invite people to the event, add a reminder, choose how you want to appear to others and even attach a picture.

- The third option is adding a task. This allows you to enter a due date for something that needs to be completed, such as writing a report. You can add priority levels and a memo or picture too.

Deleting a single or on-going calendar entry

- To delete a calendar entry, open up the event and tap the menu button, which is normally found below the screen on the left.

- Select 'Delete'. You'll see a lot of options pop up if your event is a regular one (such as a weekly/ monthly meeting), or you have invited people to the meeting.

- If this is the case, choose whether you just want to delete one occurrence, this and future occurrences or all events (whenever this event is scheduled for in the future). If you wish to inform attendees you've cancelled the event, tap the option, followed by 'OK' and the event will be deleted.

Email

The beauty of Android is that is unifies your whole Google life, including Gmail. It can also sync with every other email type, whether POP3, IMAP or Exchange. Here's how to use everything email-related on your Samsung Galaxy.

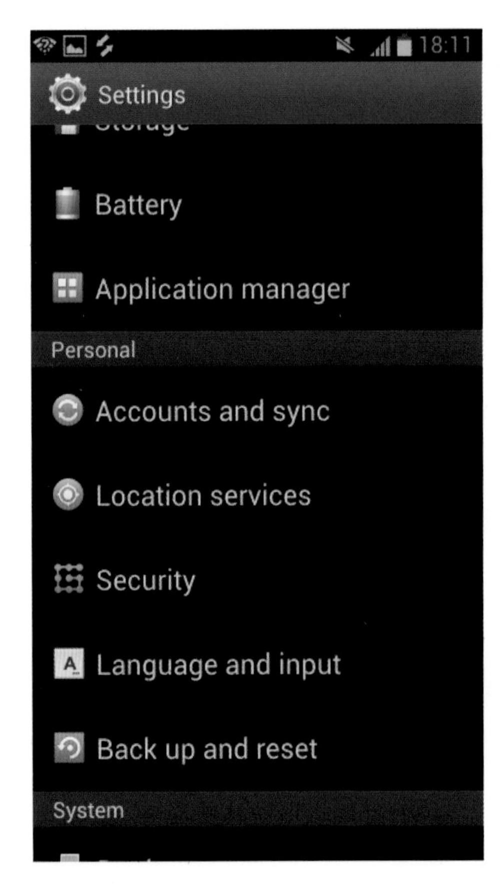

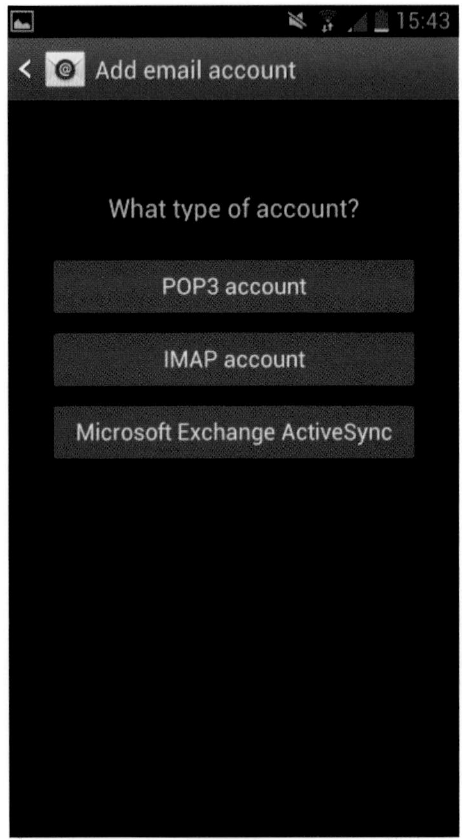

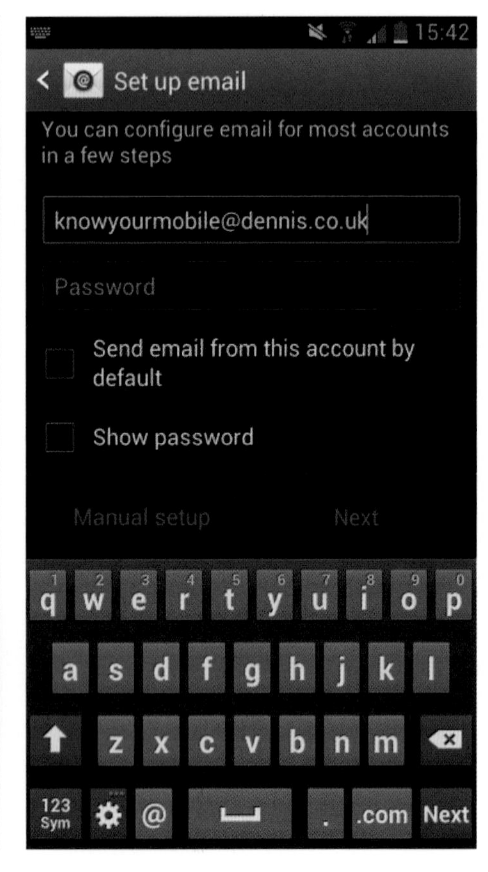

Adding an account

- You'll probably be asked to set up email when you turn on your Samsung device for the first time, but if you don't set it up then, you can do so afterwards, by tapping the email icon in your App Drawer.

- To add a new email account, head to Settings>Accounts and Personal >Add account.

Choose Email to set up a new email account

- Now enter your email address and password. If you want it to be your default email account for your device, tick the box and either select 'Next' to try and auto detect the settings (use this for accounts like Gmail, Yahoo or other web-based accounts), otherwise, select 'Manual'. You will need to know the details of the server you use to send your email.

- Choose what kind of account your email service uses. If it's a work email address, it will normally be Microsoft Exchange Activesync, but check with your company's IT department first just in case.

- Enter the Domain\Username. Ours is Dennis because our work's email domain is Dennis (knowyourmobile@dennis.co.uk). You may need to check this with your email provider though.

- You'll need to enter the server you use to send/receive email and check whether you need to use an SSL connection or not.

- Select 'Next' and accept the T&Cs.

- The server will check your settings. You'll be asked what you want to sync. We recommend email, calendar and contacts. You can also choose whether you want all your SMS messages to be sent to your email address too.

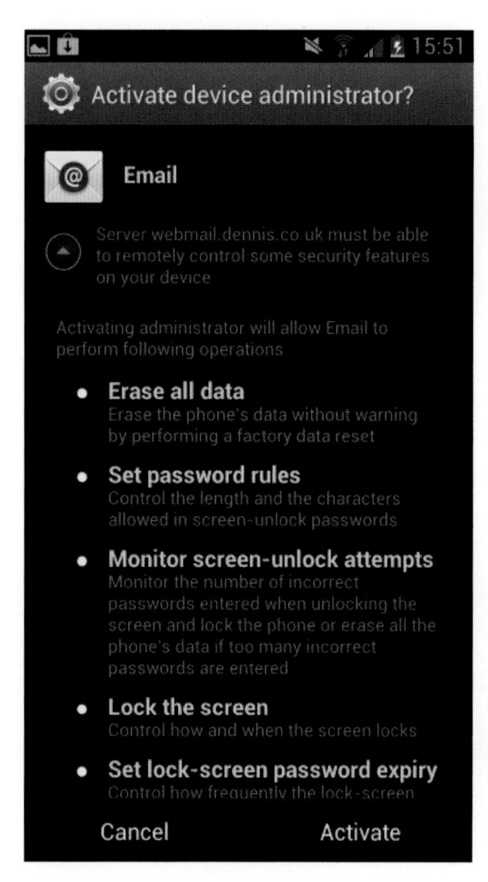

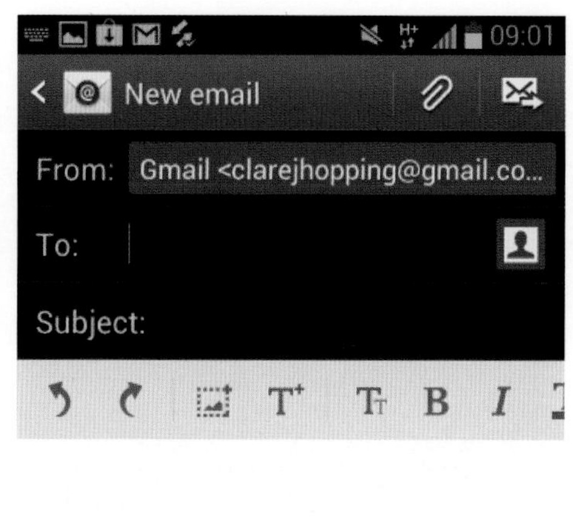

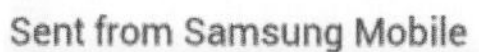

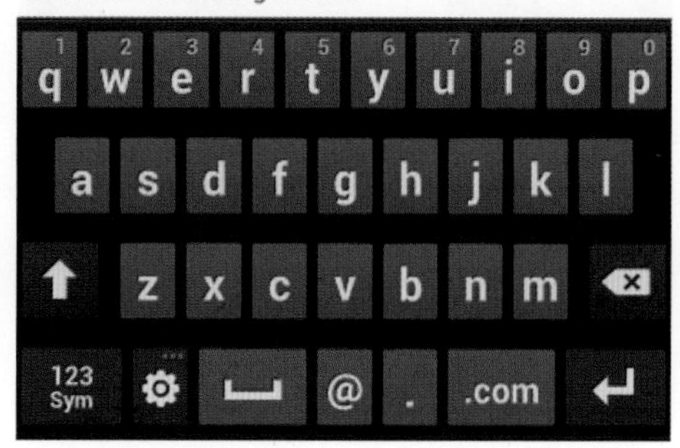

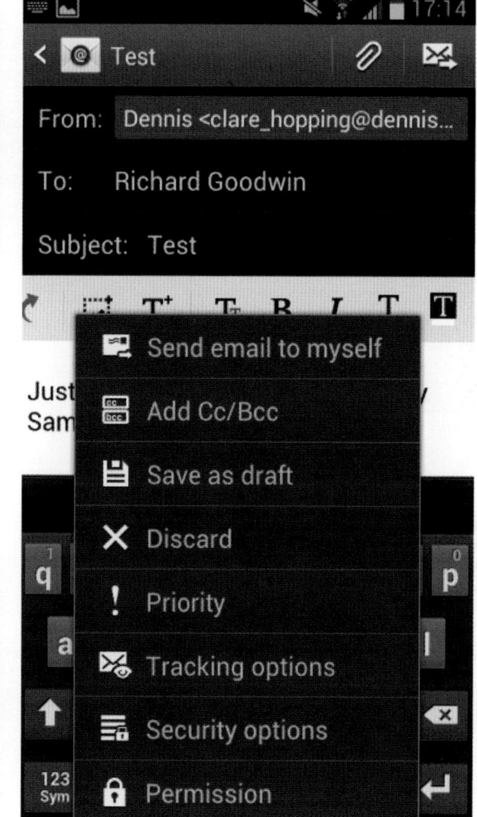

- Give the account a name and your emails will start synching.

- If you have a corporate account, you may now be asked about corporate services. Accept the device administrator settings to give your IT department access to things like remote wipe if your phone is lost or stolen. Check with your account administrator to see whether you should allow this or not.

Removing an account

- It's simple to remove an account on your Samsung Galaxy device. Head to the 'Accounts' settings from the 'Settings' menu. Now choose the account you wish to remove and select 'Remove account'.

Composing an email

- To compose an email, head to the email inbox you wish to send an email from. Now tap on the pencil icon in the top right corner.

- Type in the recipient's email address or begin typing a name from your contacts list. Alternatively, tap on the person icon and choose a group, contact from your contacts list, favourite or a contact from your recently emailed list and 'Done'.

- Now enter your email body copy. You can format the text using the tools below the subject line, and even insert a picture or add a quick response.

- To send, tap the envelope icon in the top right-hand corner.

Adding a BCC/CC

- To add a BCC or CC to your email, tap on the menu button below the screen on the bottom left-hand side and choose 'Add BCC/CC.' Enter the email address for the CC or BCC'd recipient using the same methods as when adding the recipient.

Changing priority in your email

- You can mark an email as urgent via the menu, below the screen on the right-hand side. Select 'Priority' and choose either high, medium or low.

Email

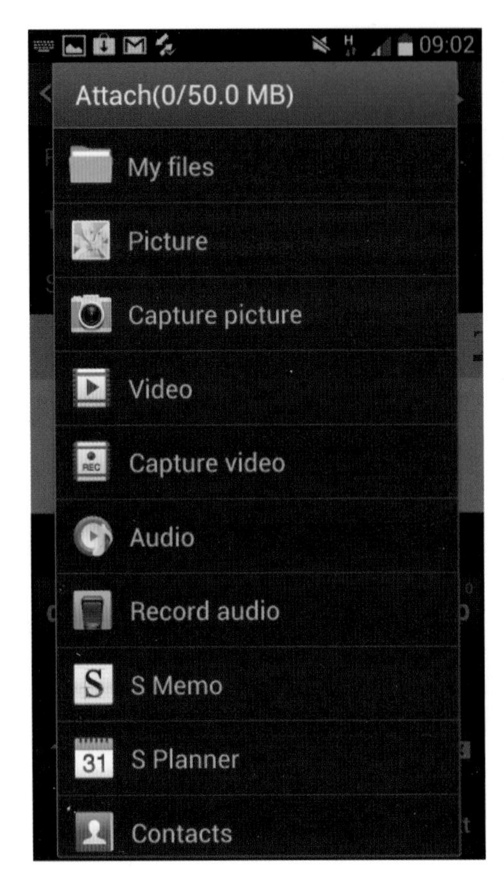

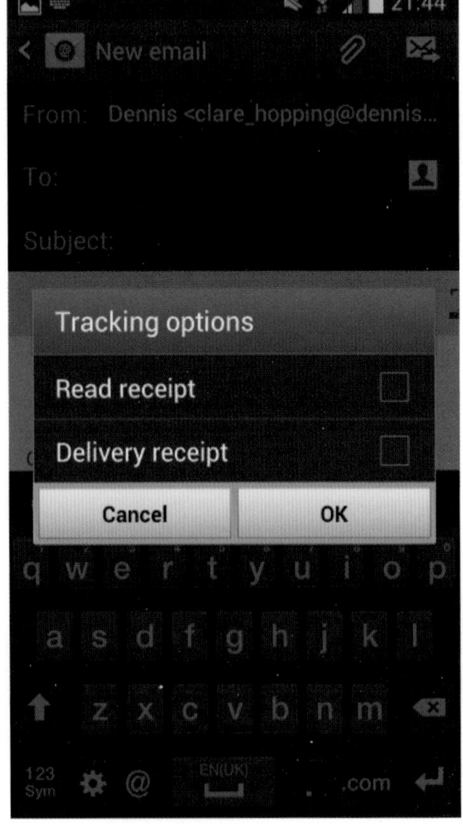

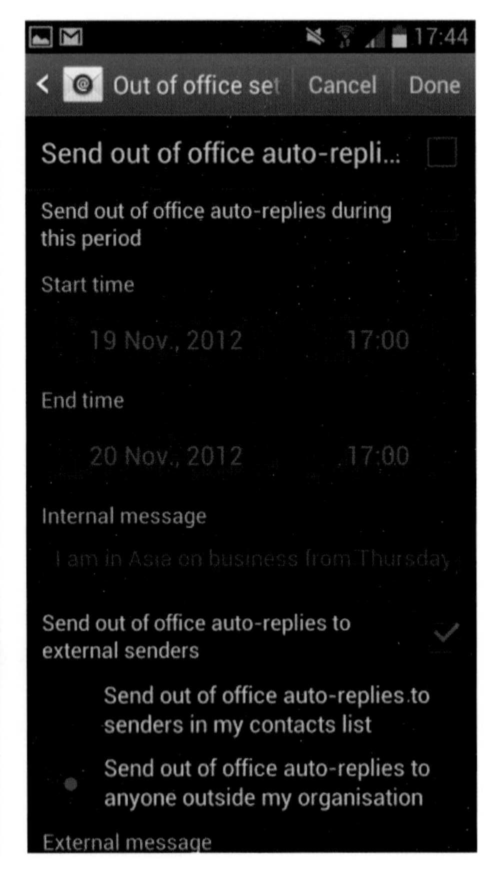

Attachments

- Adding any attachment is easy. When composing your email, just tap the paperclip icon in the top right-hand corner and select either the type of file or 'My files' to choose a file saved in that folder on your phone.

- You can also choose to attach a calendar event or contact if you wish. Samsung Galaxy devices also allow you to take a new picture or record a voice memo to attach too.

Forwarding an email

- Forwarding an email is simple. Just tap the forward icon (second from the end, top right of the screen) and enter the recipient, typing in any extra text at the top.

Getting a read notification

- If you want to be told when someone opens and reads your email, select the menu from the compose email screen, and tracking options. You can choose here to get a receipt when the email is delivered and another when the email is read.

Changing your email signature

- By default, your Samsung Galaxy device will have 'Sent from Samsung Mobile' at the bottom of the email. To change this to a personalised message, head to Settings > Accounts and sync > the email you want to modify > Settings > the email address > Signature. Now type in your new signature and ensure the slider is on.

Add an out of office auto-response

- You can add an out of office reply to any Activesync email address.

- Head to Settings > Accounts and sync > the email you want to modify > Settings > the email address and scroll down to Exchange Activesync settings. Select 'Out of office' and tap the tick-box by 'Send out of office auto-replies'.

- Enter the start time and end time, plus your personalised message. Select whether you want those inside or outside your organisation, or both to receive the response and tap 'Done'.

- Ensure you change the message in both the Internal and External boxes to make sure the message is correct for both groups.

Wi-Fi

Setting up Wi-Fi on your Samsung Galaxy will ensure you stay within the download limits set by your network. There may not always be a Wi-Fi network available, but it's best to set your device to lock to a Wi-Fi network whenever you're in range.

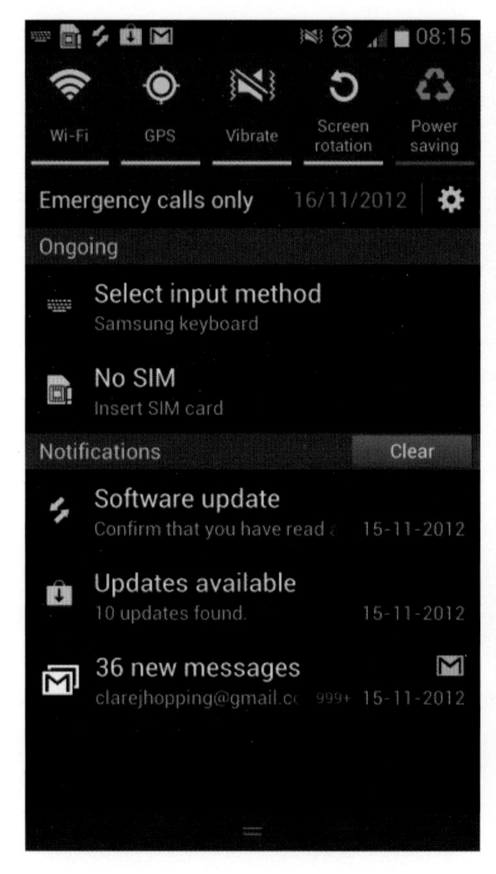

Connecting to an existing Wi-Fi network

- Pull down the taskbar from the top of the screen and select the settings icon.

- Turn on Wi-Fi and a list of available networks will appear. Choose the network you wish to connect to and enter the relevant password.

- You can turn Wi-Fi on and off by pulling down the taskbar from the top of the screen and toggle the Wi-Fi icon on or off.

Connecting to an invisible Wi-Fi network

- If your preferred network doesn't appear in the list, it may be set as invisible. If you know the name of the network, tap 'Add network' at the bottom of the screen and enter the network's SSID, security type and password if needed.

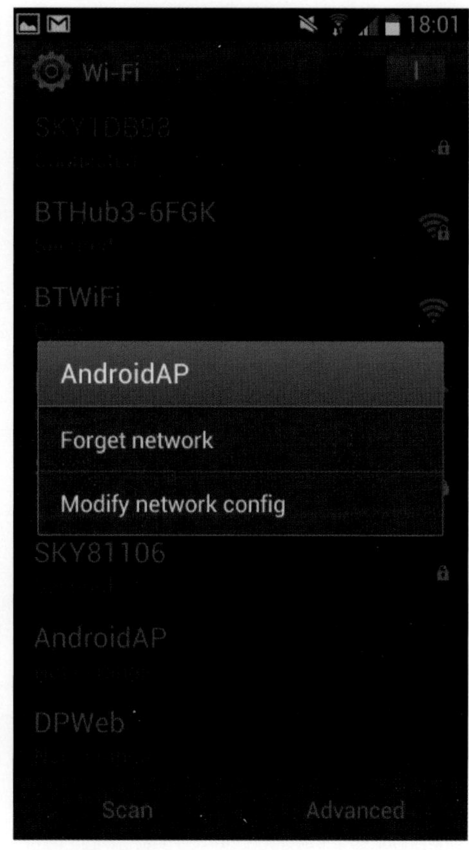

Forget networks

- If you want to stop a network showing up in your Wi-Fi list, or want to stop your phone connecting to it, long press the network in question and tap 'Forget network'.

- If you wish to add this network at a later date, force your phone to rescan for available networks by tapping 'Scan' at the bottom of the Wi-Fi menu.

Setting up a Wi-Fi hotspot

Most Samsung Galaxy devices support Wi-Fi hotspots, allowing you to connect to the internet on your laptop or other mobile devices using its network data connection. Be warned though – although it's useful, you need to carefully monitor your data usage because it is very easy to go over your limits and end up with a huge data bill at the end of the month.

- To set up a Wi-Fi hotspot connection, head to Settings > More settings (under the wireless and networks section) > Tethering and portable hotspot.

- Turn on 'Portable Wi-Fi hotspot' and tap 'Configure'. Here you can change the connection name to something memorable and change the password required when another device wants to connect. You can also choose to hide your device but you will need to search for it manually from your laptop or other device.

- From your laptop or other device, search for a Wi-Fi connection. You should be able to find the network in seconds - it will have the name you just set on your Galaxy device. Enter the password and you should now be connected.

Top Secret Tip

Phone running a little slow? Close some apps. Head to the multitasking screen by long holding the home button and all your open apps will pop up. Close them by swiping the 'cards' off the screen. They'll now be closed and your device will speed along.

Synching and backup

It's important to sync and backup your Galaxy device, just in case something goes wrong and you need to restore the data on your device, or you change devices.

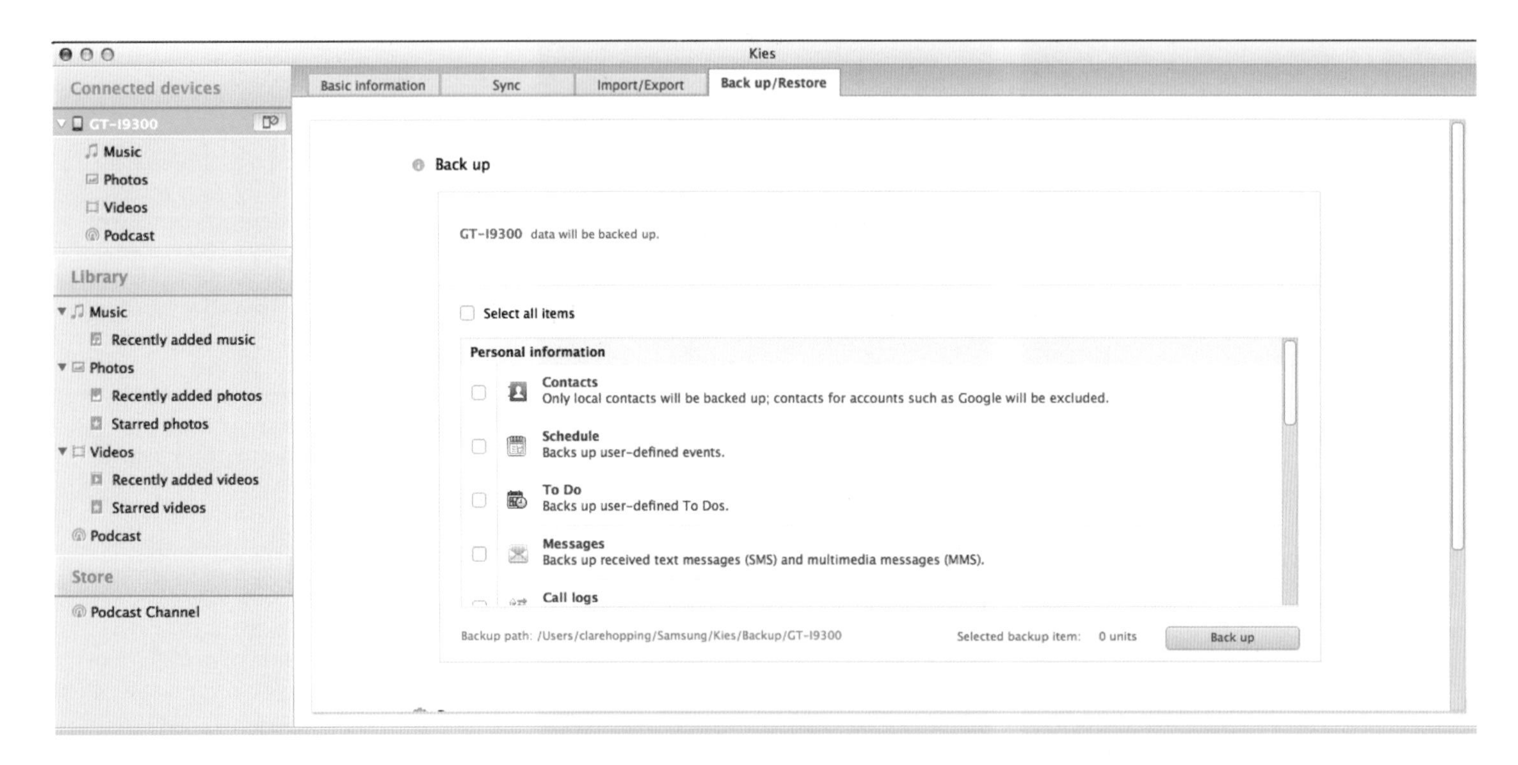

Kies overview

Samsung Kies is the Samsung backup and restore programme that ships with Samsung devices. It's available for Mac and PC.

Backing up with Kies

Kies allows you to back up all of your data to your device so you can restore it later if you need to rest your phone or if it malfunctions. It's so simple to do.

- Open up the Kies software on your computer and plug your phone in using the USB cable provided with your device.
- Kies should detect your device in the upper left-hand corner.
- Navigate to 'Backup' and select the items you want to back up by selecting the tick next to each item. You can back up almost everything, from your messages, to call logs, contacts, memos, music, applications and photos.
- Once you've selected what you want to back up, just tap Back up and the back up will start. Do not unplug your phone when this is happening as it can ruin your handset.

Restoring with Kies

- To restore your device after performing a hard reset or if you wish to go back to an earlier back up of your device, navigate to 'Back up/Restore' and scroll down to 'Restore'.
- Select the back-up file you wish to use to restore your phone and select 'OK'.
- Your device will now restore and any data not on the back-up file will be replaced.

Top Secret Tip

Save some battery juice by reducing the brightness of the screen and turning off 3G, Wi-Fi and Bluetooth when you're not using them. You can also turn off location services by heading to Settings > Location services > untick Use wireless networks, Use GPS and Location and Google search.

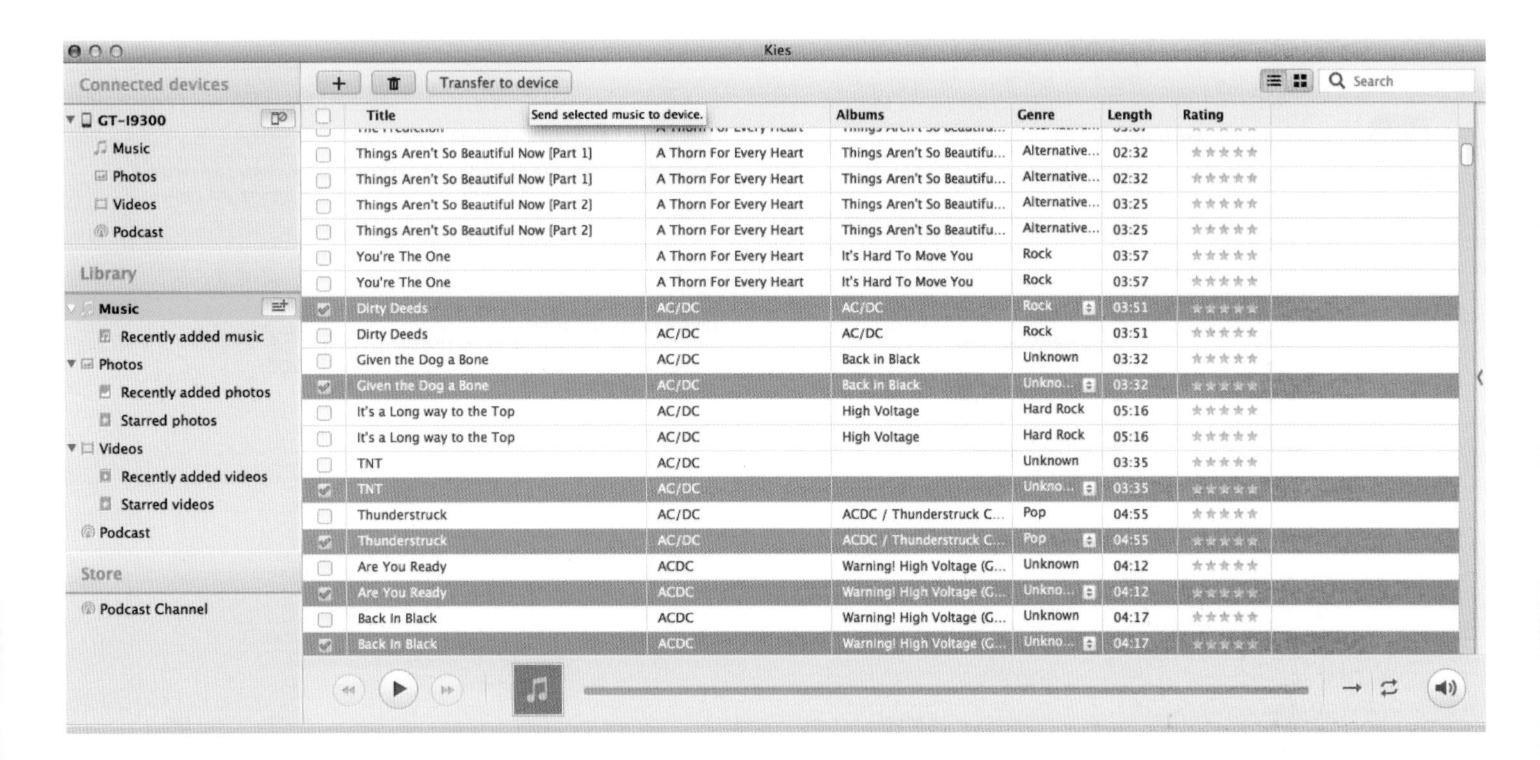

Synching with Kies

Kies allows you to sync your music, photos and videos from your PC with your phone.

- When you first start-up the Kies software, it will ask whether you want it to import all your music by searching your computer's hard drive or you can specify a particular folder. Once you've made your decision it will search your computer finding any relevant music files in the library.

- Now, you can add all or some of this music to your device. Select 'Music' and choose the artists or track you wish to add to your device. You can, of course, select all, but those with DRM protection will not be transferred.

- Now select 'Transfer to device' and the music will be transferred, providing there's enough free space on your handset.

- You can transfer photos and videos in exactly the same way.

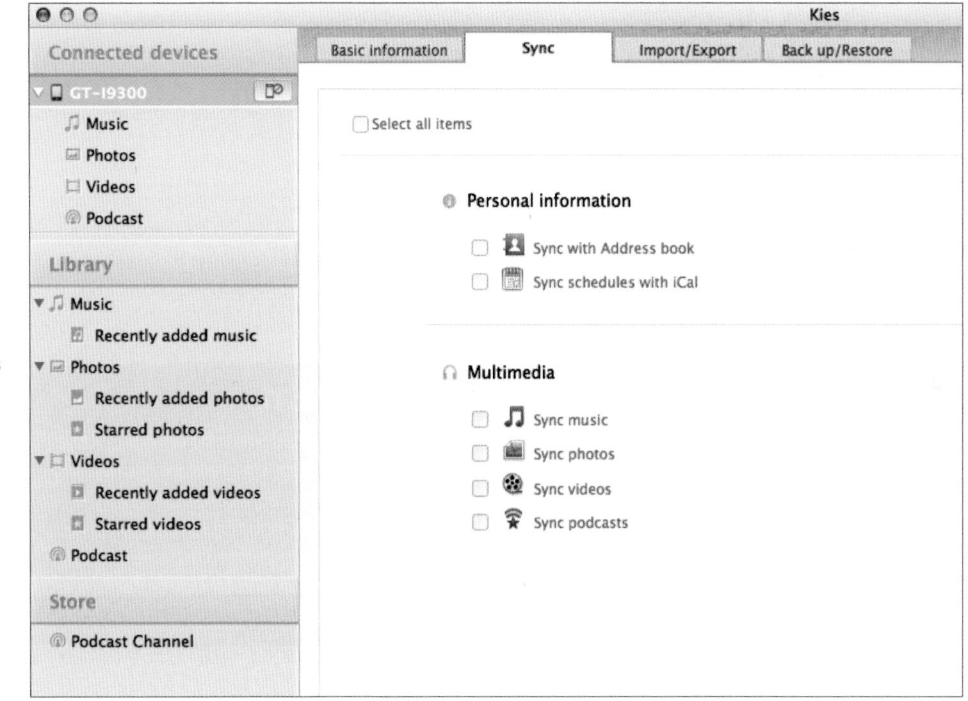

Updating the firmware on your Galaxy

It's pretty important to update the firmware on your Samsung Galaxy device whenever one becomes available because not only will it give you new and exciting features, it'll also keep your device bug-free and running smoothly too.

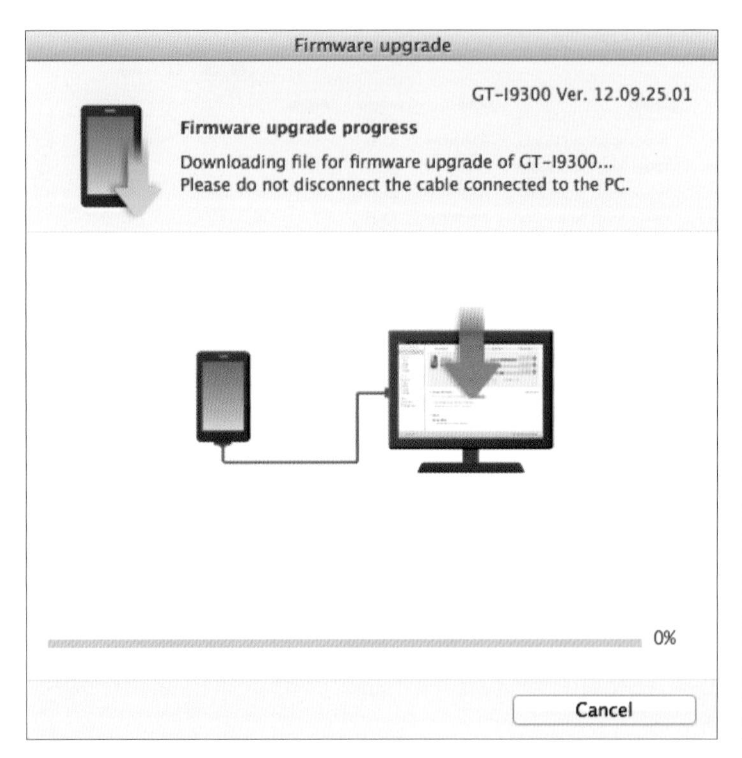

Updating the firmware on your computer via Kies

- If an update is available for your Samsung Galaxy device, a message will pop up when you first plug your handset into your computer. It should read: 'A new firmware version is available. Upgrading may improve performance of [phone name]. Do you want to upgrade?' along with the current version of the firmware and the version ready for upgrade. Select 'Update' to proceed. You will then be presented with a warning. Read this carefully and go ahead with the upgrade if you agree.

- The upgrade will then download and your phone will restart. Do not unplug your phone during the update as this can destroy your phone.

- When the upgrade is complete, your phone will turn back on and you will be presented with a 'firmware upgrade is complete' message. You can now continue using your phone.

Updating the firmware on your phone over the air (OTA)

If a firmware update is available for your phone and it supports over the air (OTA) upgrades, you will be alerted in the toolbar.

- Tap the firmware update notification to update the firmware on your phone. We recommend you connect via Wi-Fi as some firmware updates are large and may force you to go over your network's data limit.

Top Secret Tip

Simplify your homescreen by enabling Easy homescreen. To turn this feature on, head to Settings > Home screen mode > Easy homescreen. You'll find the homescreen is now a lot more straightforward and easier to read and you can add favourite contacts, settings and apps easily.

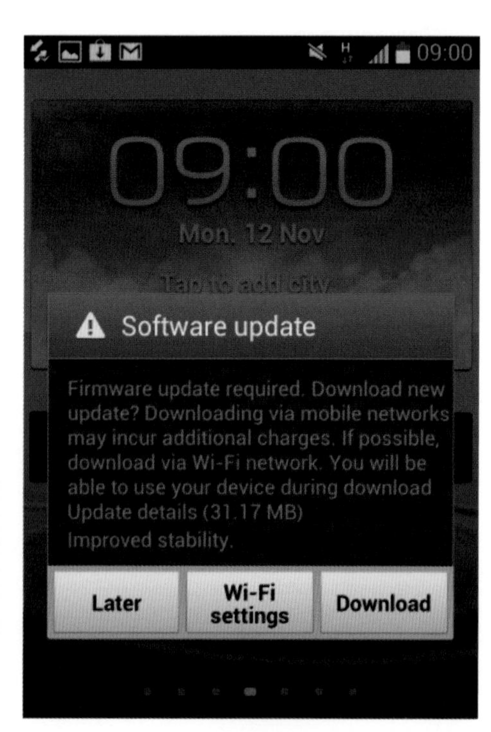

Chapter 4

Applications

How to use Google Play: Setting up, Searching, and Downloading

With an Android-powered Galaxy device there's a whole world of entertainment at your fingertips. Google's Play store houses some 600,000-plus applications and games, as well as the latest eBooks, films, TV shows, and magazines.

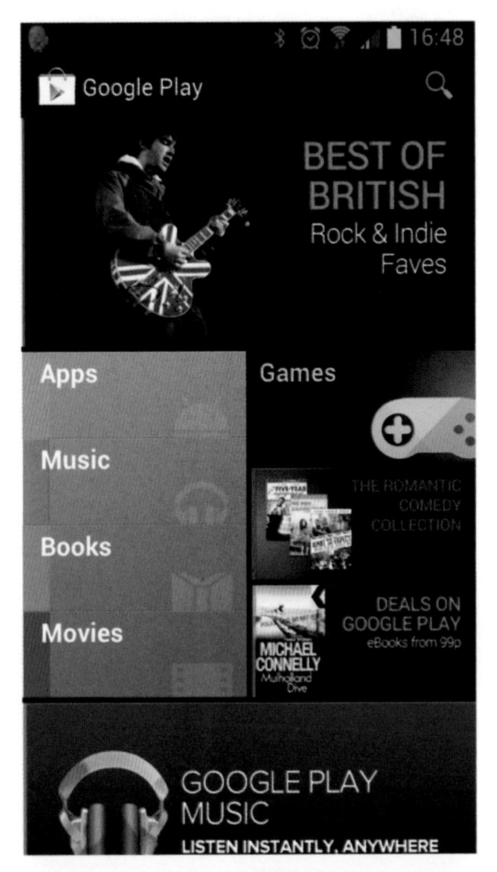

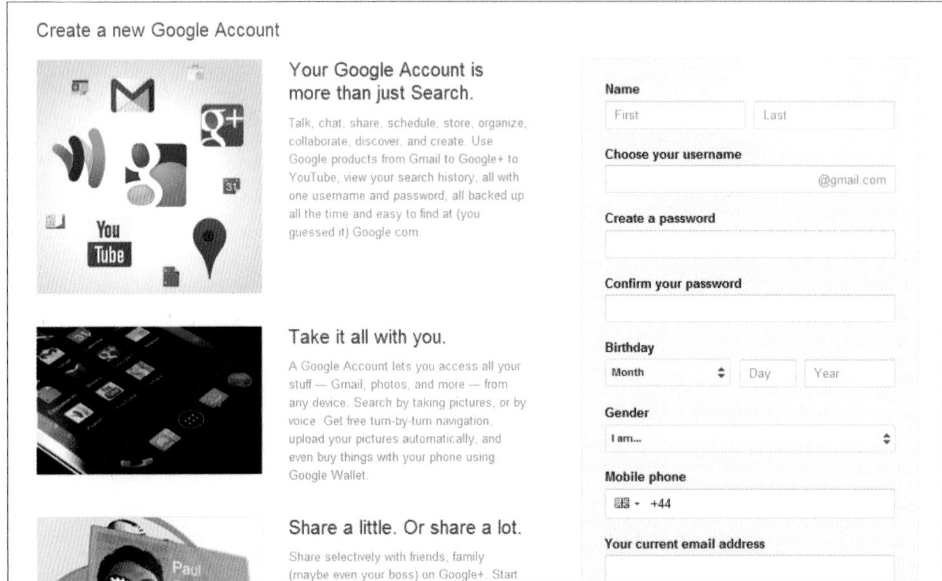

Top Secret Tip

You can take a screenshot on almost any Samsung Galaxy device, whether you want to show off your gaming talents or show people what they're missing. Just press the power button and home key, on Samsung-branded handsets or the volume down and power key on the Galaxy Nexus.

Google's Play store has more free content than any other platform so you can fill your handset or tablet up with tons of useful content without spending a penny. There's also plenty of premium content too, including console-like gaming, productivity applications, and tools for professional users.

You can also buy and rent films and TV shows for either viewing on your Galaxy device or a connected Samsung HDTV.

Google's Play store is also available online via your PC's web browser. Once logged into Play on your browser you can download content and sync it with your smartphone and tablet. Perfect.

So whether it's films, gaming, TV, applications, or literature, Google Play has it covered. Next, we'll show you how to set-up the Play store on your Galaxy device and how to use it correctly.

Setting up Google Play

Before you can access Google's Play store or use your Galaxy smartphone or tablet to its full potential you'll need to sign-up for a Google account.

Having a Google account gets you access to all of Google's services – Gmail, Drive, Music, YouTube, and Reader – and it also saves all of your contacts, apps, and emails to the cloud, so you can switch between devices with ease.

Setting up a Google Account

The easiest way to create a Google account is on your PC by opening up Google and selecting the 'sign up' option in the top right-hand side of your browser.

Fill in the relevant details – name, desired email address, and password – and you're done. Now all your emails, contacts, apps, games and calendar entries will be synced across all your devices. Just sign-in with your Google account and they will be there.

Setting up a Google Play account on your device

- Open Google Play
- You'll now be prompted to 'Add a Google Account'
- Select 'New'
- Enter your first and last name, select 'Done'
- Enter your desired email address
- Create a password
- Choose a security question and enter a recovery email address – this can be any email account you're currently using
- You'll be invited to join Google+
- Click 'Next', and you're done

Sign-in to Google Play

Now that your Galaxy device is all set-up, you'll want to start populating it with applications, games, books and movies. But before you can go exploring inside one of the world's largest digital content lockers, you'll need to sign-in with your newly acquired Google credentials.

Here's how it's done:

- Tap the Google Play icon on your Galaxy device
- Now you'll be prompted to 'Add a Google Account'
- Enter your Google Account details – email and password
- Follow the instructions – your device will guide you through the rest

Top Secret Tip

Samsung Jelly Bean devices feature a little hidden time-waster game. Just head to Settings > About device > Tap on Android version and jelly beans will fill the screen. You can swipe, flick and play with the little cartoon icons. It's seriously addictive and you have been warned!

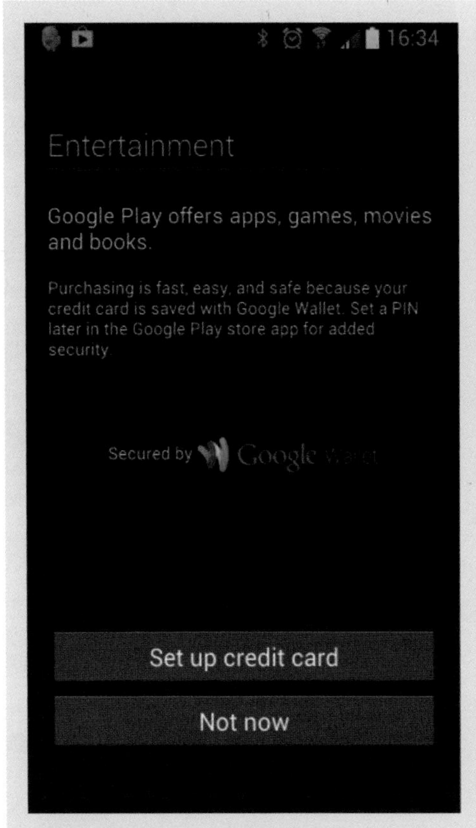

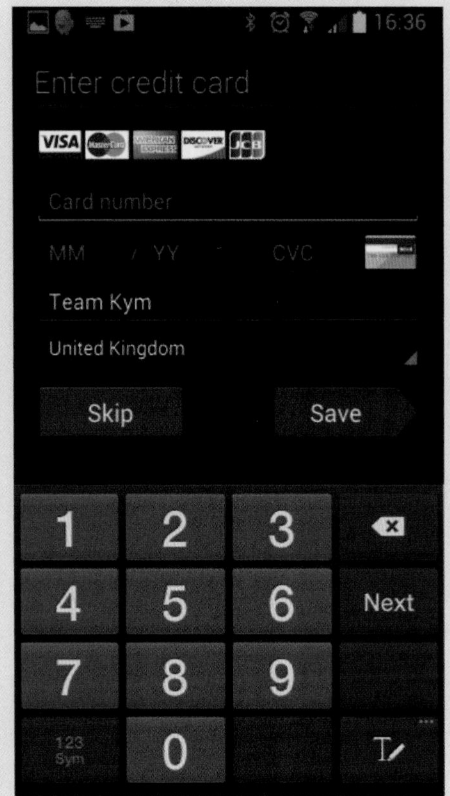

Setting-up Google Wallet

To pay for content on Google Play – be it applications, games, themes, magazines, books, TV shows or films – you'll need to set up Google Wallet.

Google Wallet is a digital payment system that enables you to purchase content directly from the Play store with one click. All you need to do is attach your credit or debit card to your Google Account.

But, before you sign-up to Google Wallet, please ensure your credit/debit card is supported. Google Wallet accepts the following types of card:

- American Express
- Discover
- MasterCard
- Visa
- Visa Electron

Because your account is new and doesn't have a credit/debit card saved to it, Google will prompt you to set up a payment method once you've signed in.

- Select 'Set up credit card'
- Enter you card's details and follow the on-screen instructions
- Once you're signed-in successfully, you'll be presented with a variety of sync options – select the ones you want to be synced with your device

Now that you've registered with Google, signed in to the Play store, and added a payment method you're ready to go off and explore everything that's on offer inside.

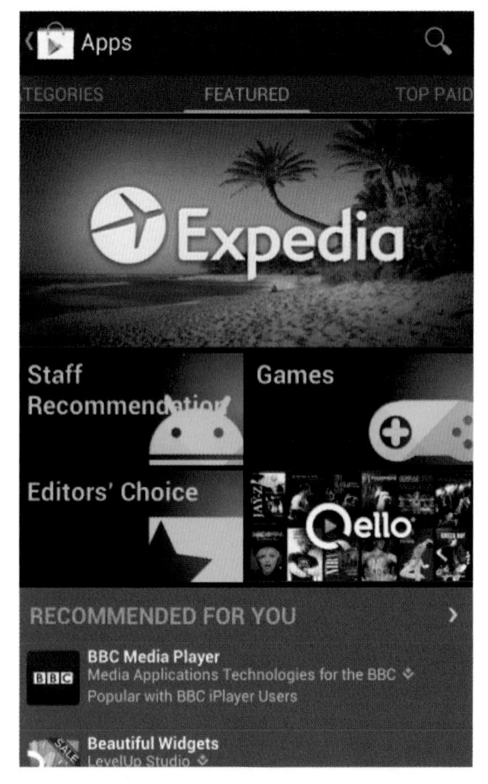

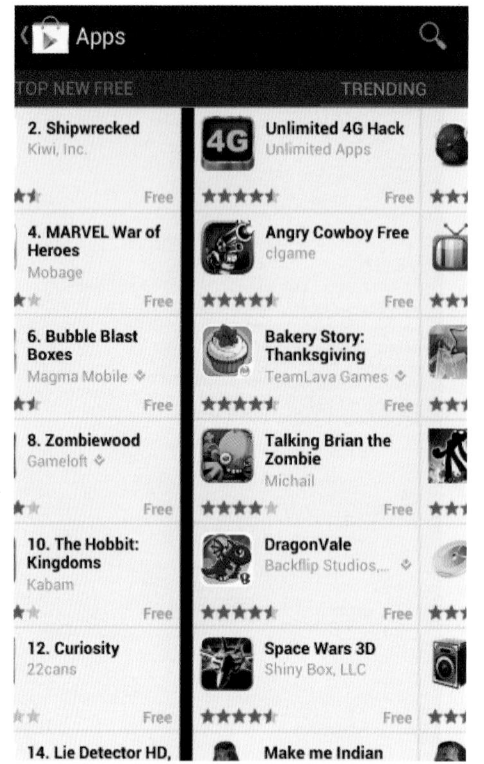

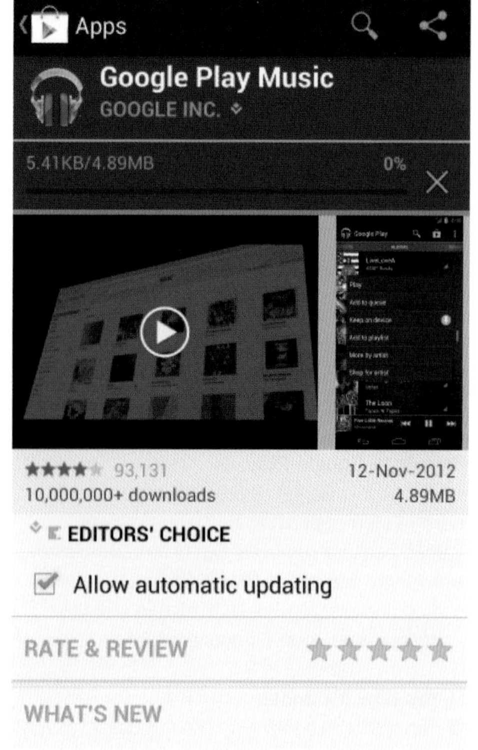

Searching Google Play

Google breaks all of its published content down into sections: Apps, Music, Books, and Movies. Open the Play store and you'll see them running down the left-hand side of your display.

Google Play also aggregates all the latest content from its legions of publishers, with top content, new releases, and deals taking centre stage on the app's homepage.

Know what you're looking for?

- Hit the 'Search' icon – it's located in the top right-hand corner
- Select the content and you'll be taken to a download page
- Click 'Install' and the application will be downloaded to your device

Browsing?

The Play store is an excellent place to browse for new applications and games as there's always so much to choose from, and everything is broken down into logical, easy-to-navigate categories and sections.

Let's look at Apps

From the Play store's homepage, select 'Apps.' Inside here you have a few options:
Featured – New applications are displayed everyday here, complete with a banner image
Staff Recommendations – A curated list of all the best apps out there
Editor's Choice – Another list of hand-picked applications
Games – This takes you through to the Games section

Exploring Apps

Google aggregates content across all sections in its Play store based on ratings, pricing, and how many times they've been downloaded. That way you can see what's most popular with fellow Android users around the globe.

Navigating

- Swipe from left-to-right to reveal Categories
- Swipe right-to-left to see Top Paid content
- Another swipe right will reveal Top Free content
- Another, Top Grossing
- Another, Top New Paid
- Another, Top New Free
- And finally, Trending

Please note: all of these navigation processes apply to all areas of the Play store – Apps, Games, Music, Books, and Movies.

When you've found the application, game, film, book, or TV show you want to download, simply click the install or price icon, click the 'Accept & Download' option and your application will install.

You can also preview a video of the content, as well as pictures and user reviews, before downloading. Like what you've downloaded? Why not Google+ it so others can see your recommendation by tapping the G+ icon.

You'll know your Google Play content is downloading when an icon appears on the top left-hand side of Galaxy device – it's a down-pointing animated arrow. Once the content has completed download it will appear on one of your device's homescreens or inside your apps menu.

Books, Films, and TV will be added to Google Music, Play Books and Play Movies' respective libraries. To access this content simply open the application and the new media should be in there. Simple.

Samsung Apps overview

With an Android-powered Galaxy device you have two application stores at your disposal in the form of Google Play and Samsung Apps.

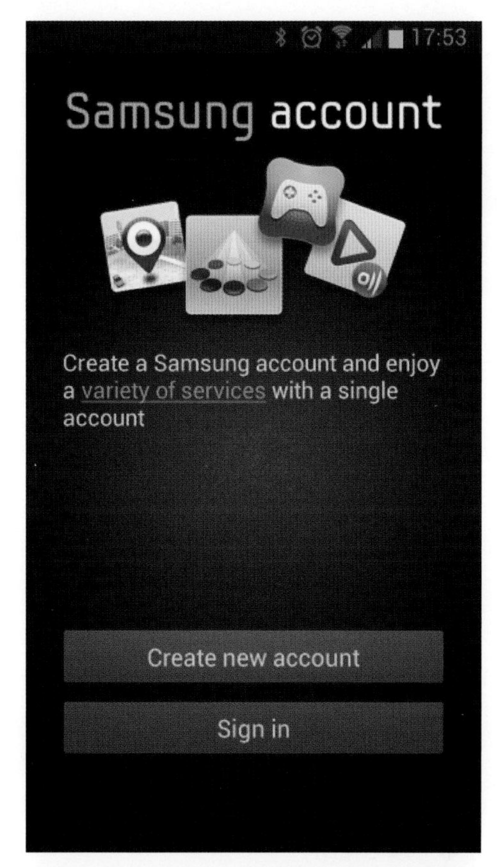

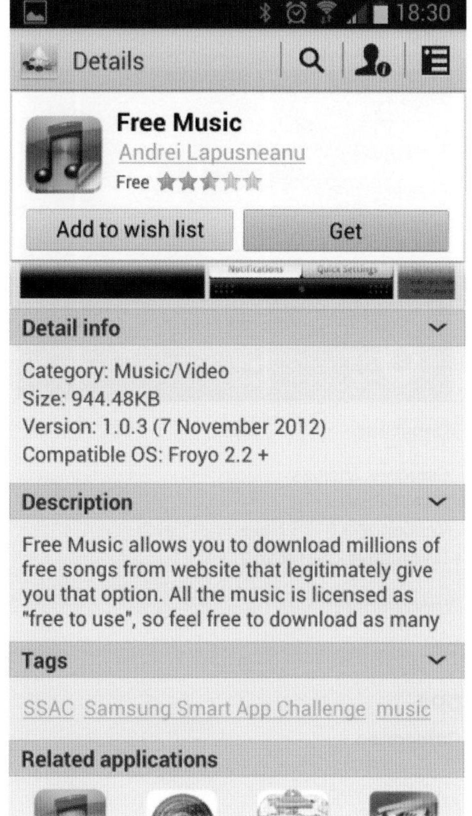

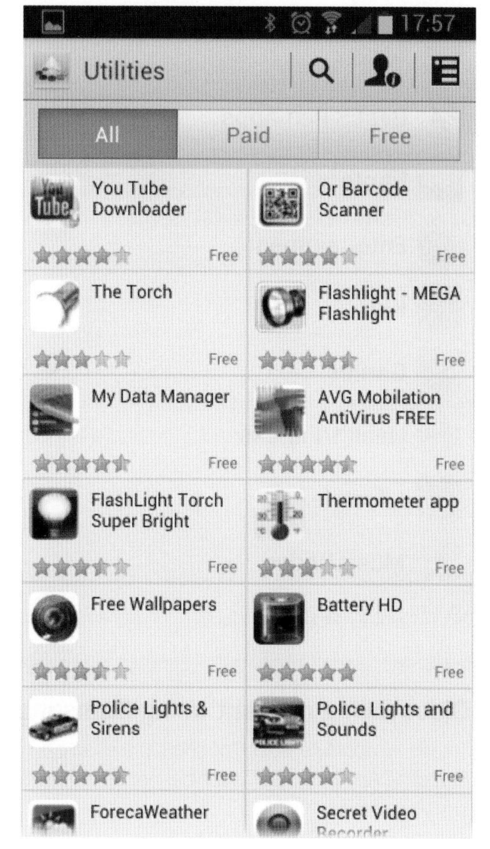

Top Secret Tip

If you use Dropbox on your computer, make sure you set up the cloud storage service on your Samsung Galaxy device. You'll be able to access your cloud-based files wherever you are, plus you'll be rewarded with an additional 50GB storage at no cost whatsoever.

With Samsung Apps you can download specific content for your device to make it even smarter. You'll also get exclusive access to offers that aren't available anywhere else, such as free downloads on big-name content and a whole host of other deals for handset add-ons that can be used with S-Pen, for example.

Here, we'll show you how to set up Samsung Apps and how to get the most out of the service.

Setting up Samsung Apps

To access everything Samsung Apps has to offer you'll first need to set up an account. Here's how that's done:

Please note: if you didn't set-up a Samsung Apps account when you first activated your phone, simply attempt to buy an application and you'll be asked to register.

- Select 'Create new account'
- Tick the 'I accept all the terms above' box
- Hit 'Agree'
- Fill in the relevant details as prompted: email, password, name, etc
- Select 'Sign up' and you're done
- Welcome to Samsung Apps

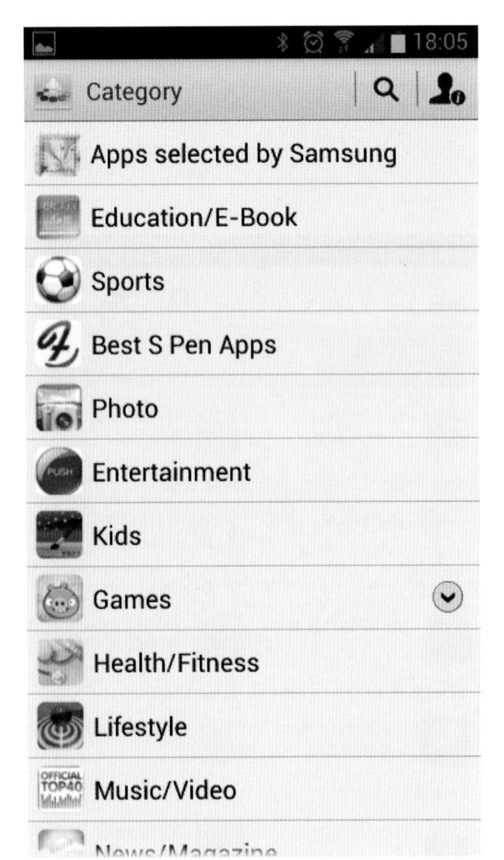

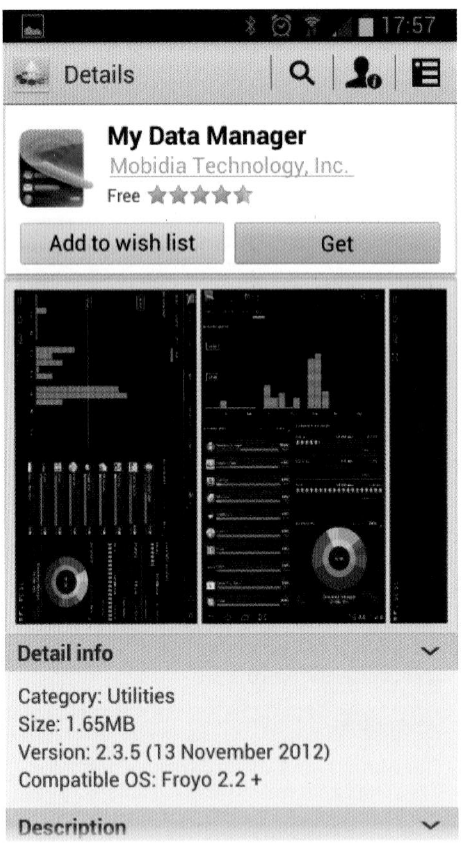

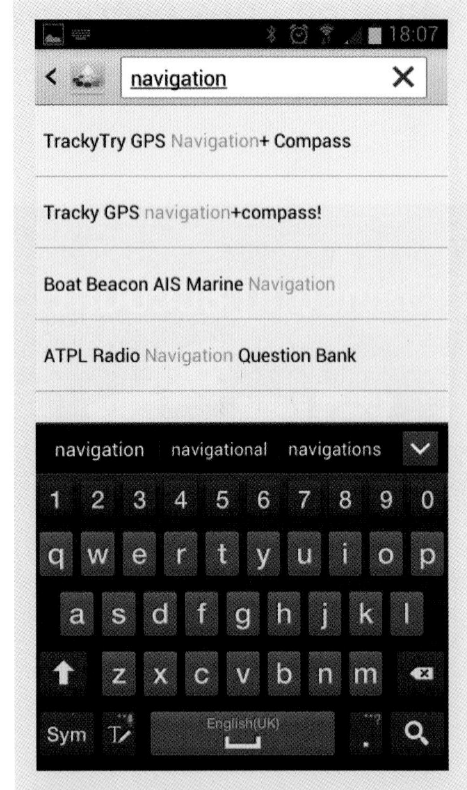

Discovering content using Samsung Apps

There's an absolute wealth of content available on Samsung Apps, some of which cannot be found anywhere else.

It's also simple to get the content downloaded and running on your Galaxy device as the entire store works in a similar fashion to Google's Play portal.

Open Samsung Apps and the first thing you'll see is a colourful carousel which displays all the latest apps, games and media available inside the portal.

Below this you'll find Samsung Apps' main categories: **Hot, Top, New, and Promos** – here you'll find all the latest and greatest titles currently on offer. Each section can be expanded, simply by clicking 'More', to reveal a larger selection of apps.

Categories

To view individual categories inside Samsung Apps just hit the 'Categories' icon in the top right corner.

Inside Categories you'll find everything from the best S-Pen apps to lifestyle and utilities apps and more – it's all there.

Every section is broken up into three sub sections: 'All', 'Paid', and 'Free'. Select the option you wish to see and you'll be presented with a selection of applications – scroll downwards to view the entire collection

Search

If you know exactly what you're looking for or at least have a vague idea about the type or style of content you're after, you can just search for it manually inside Samsung Apps by tapping the 'Search' icon.

- Type in your search query, say: 'Navigation'
- Click 'Search'
- Samsung Apps will now display all content that includes the term 'Navigation' inside its description below your query

Installing Apps

- Once you've located the app you want, select it. This will take you to its home page – here you can read reviews, see screen shots, and read a description of the app
- Select 'Get' to download
- Like with Google Play, the download progress of the app can be viewed in the drop-down notifications window
- Once the application is downloaded it'll either be posted to one of your home screens or appear inside your app menu
- Enjoy!

50 must-have apps

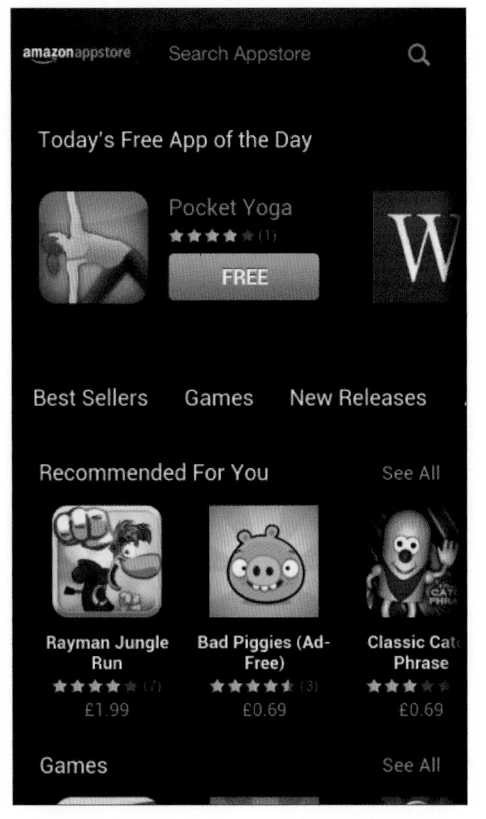

Amazon App Store

Free

Download Amazon's App Store for a free paid app every day - it's really that simple. Unlike the rest of the apps in our top 50, the Amazon App store has to be downloaded through the Amazon website, though once installed, it's a breeze to use and functions like all the rest.

Astrid

Free

Astrid at its most basic level enables you to add and check-off tasks like any good task manager. With support for multiple lists, online editing and syncing with your Gmail account, it also packs a lot more organisational punch, separating it from the pack.

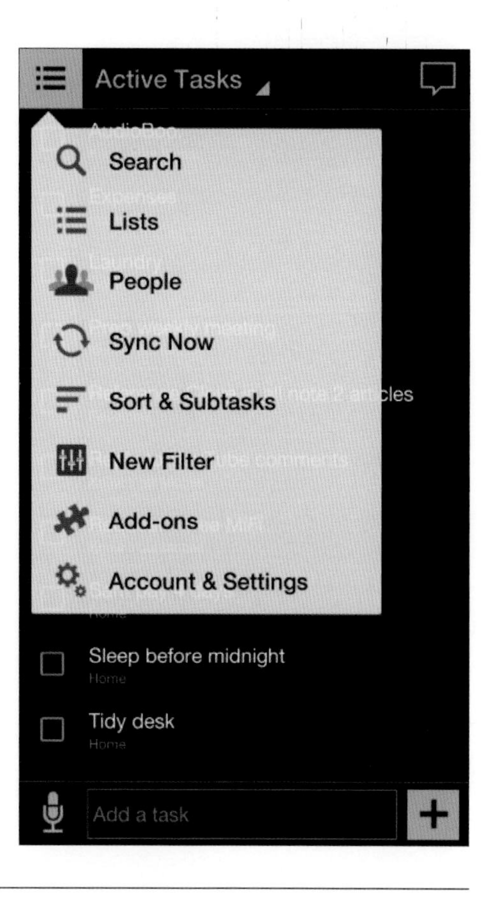

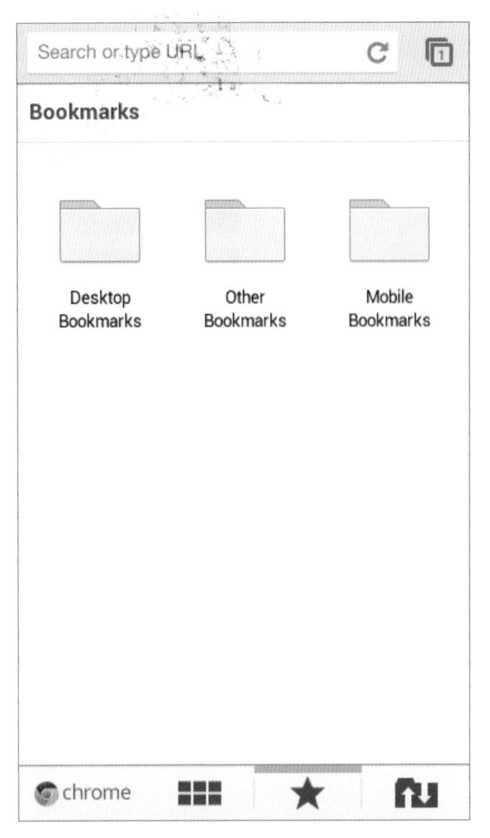

Chrome
Free

Chrome for Android synchronises with Chrome for desktop, bringing all your bookmarks, search history and browsing habits to your mobile with little more than your username and password. A must-have for all Chrome desktop users.

Dropbox
Free

Dropbox is your drive in the cloud. Giving you 2GB of data for free, you can upload and access your files from anywhere thanks to the Android app. If you've got a Samsung Galaxy S III or Note 2, you'll also get 50GB free Dropbox storage for two years by simply logging in.

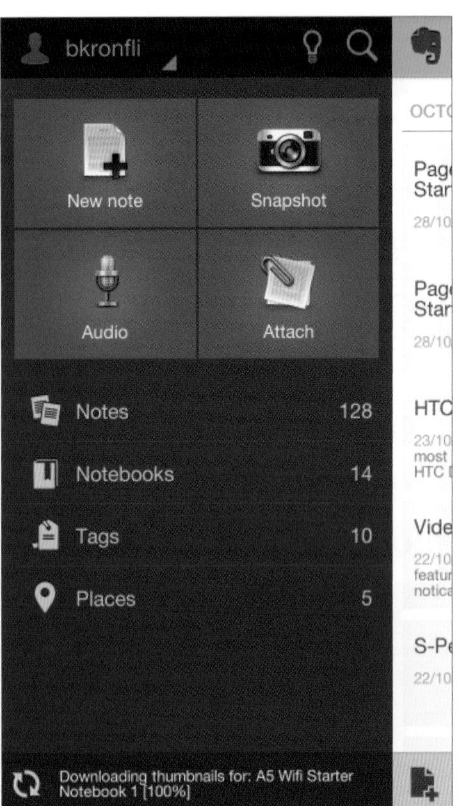

Evernote
Free

For robust cloud note taking, it doesn't get much better than Evernote. Combining text, pictures, audio and even sketches into a single note, the Evernote app on your Android is the perfect way to make notes on the go.

ezPDF Reader
£2.50

Harnessing all the cores in your Galaxy device, ezPDF Reader opens PDFs speedily and even enables document signing, marking up, highlighting and box-checking in forms. Once edited, save your PDF in a range of formats, email it and get on with your day.

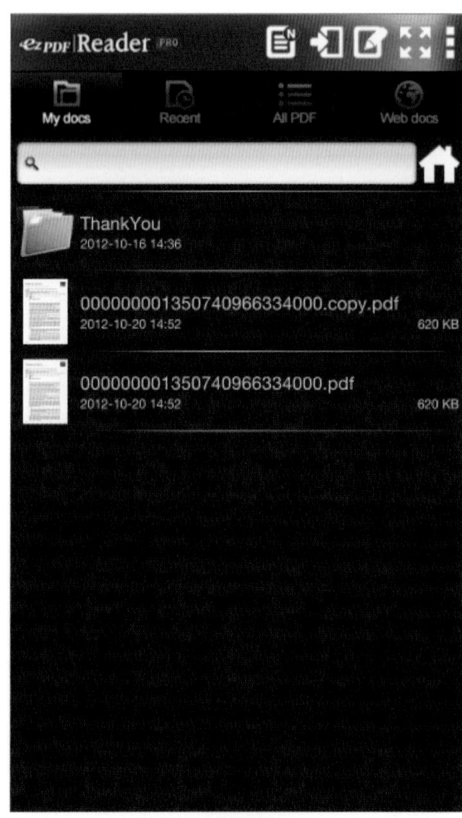

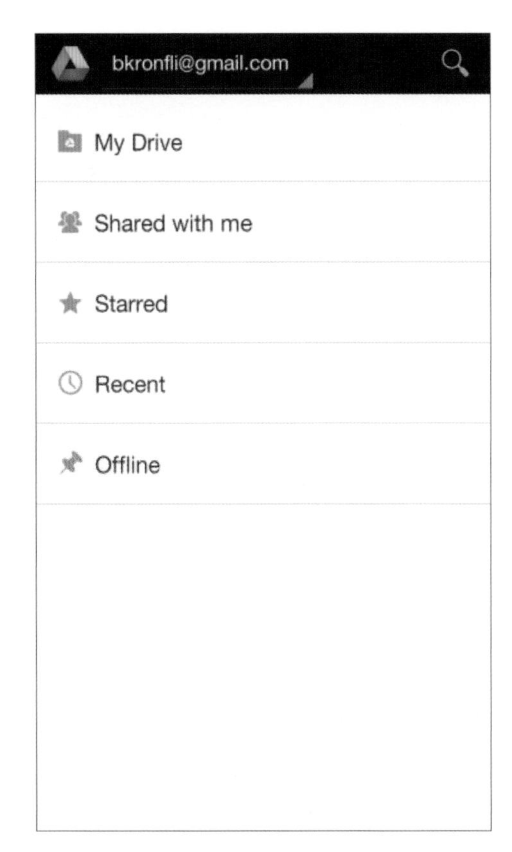

Google Drive
Free

Google Drive is an online office suite. Create, edit and share documents while at a computer or on your phone using the Drive app. Drive supports offline editing, then when your connection is restored, seamlessly syncs changes with your Google account.

gReader Pro
£3.19

gReader pro is an advanced Google Reader app. Complete with night mode, podcast support and a scrollable widget, it's considerably more comprehensive than Google's own reader app. gReader even auto-caches posts, so whether you're connected or not, you can be up to date with all the latest news.

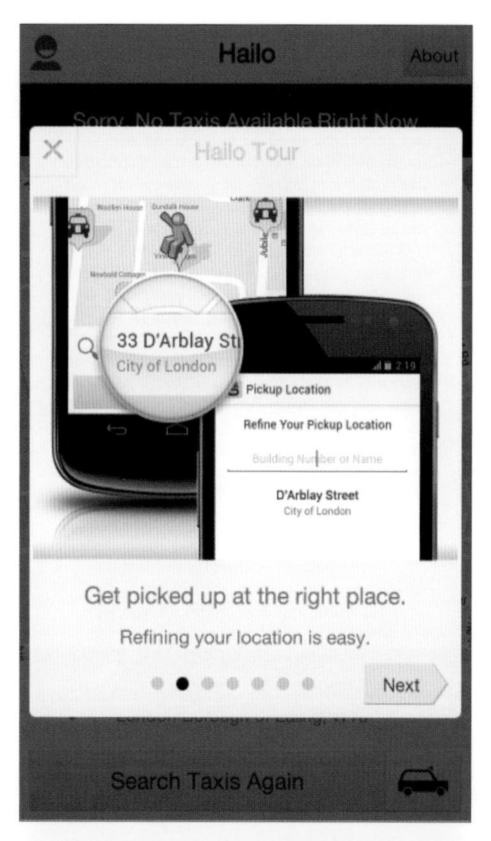

Hailo
Free

Why traverse the streets in search of a taxi when the Hailo app brings the taxi to you? Tapping into a network of London's black cabs, Hailo shows you where your nearest cab is, calls it and even lets you pay and tip the driver digitally.

Infinite Painter
£3.13

Perfectly suited to Samsung Galaxy Note devices and their S Pens, Infinite Painter applies colour to your canvas just like a paint brush would. You can create real works of art by blending colours over one another and creating oil-paint like images.

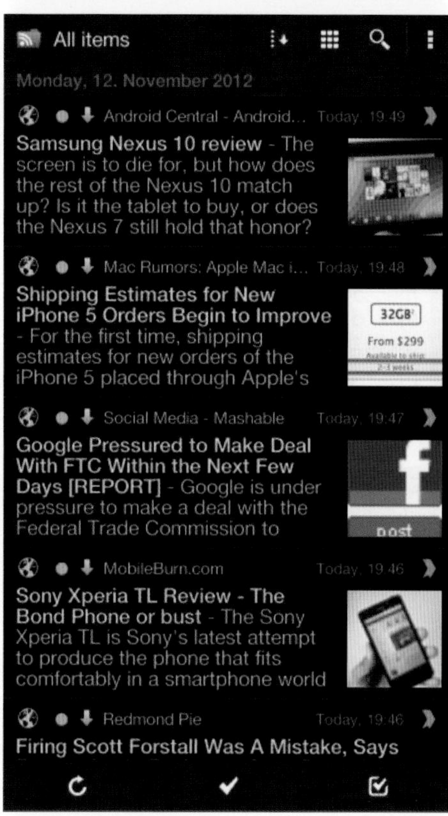

GETTING THINGS DONE: HOW TO ACHIEVE STRESS-...
Chapter 1 A New Practice for a New Reality

—where and when you'll go, what you'll do, how to prepare for the trip, and so on. Or you and your boss need to make some decisions about the new departmental reorganization you're about to launch. Or you just need to get your thinking up to date on the customer you're about to call. This is "project planning" in the broad sense. It's focusing in on a single endeavor, situation, or person and fleshing out whatever ideas, details, priorities, and sequences of events may be required for you to handle it, at least for the moment.

The goal for managing horizontally and vertically is the same: to get things off your mind and get things done. Appropriate action management lets you feel comfortable and in control as you move through your broad spectrum of work and life, while appropriate project focusing gets you clear about and on track with the specifics needed.

There is usually an inverse proportion between how much something is on your mind and how much it's getting done.

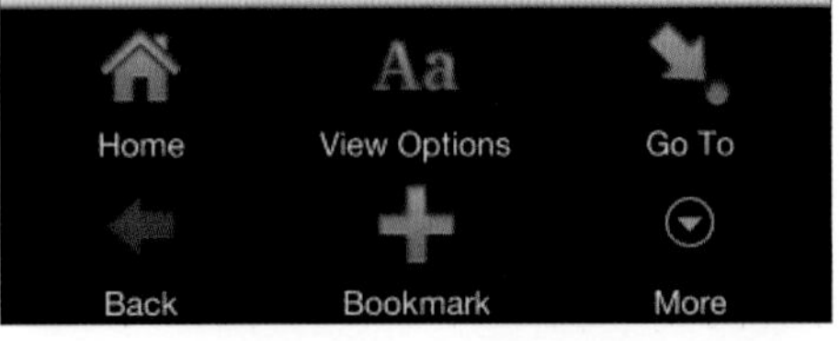

Kindle
Free

The Kindle app gives you instant access to more than a million books, newspapers, magazines and blogs wherever you are, working across multiple platforms. Just download it, sign-in and get either paid-for or free books to start reading.

LayerPaint
£1.99

LayerPaint is the app for the comic book artist in you. As the name suggests, it provides layers upon which to work. Sketching, airbrushing and inking, you can do it all in LayerPaint and even export your creation to a multi-layered PSD file.

50 must-have apps

MightyText
Free

Not a fan of touchscreen typing? Get MightyText. Once installed on your phone, just log onto the MightyText website on your computer and you'll be able to send, receive and read texts without eye strain, and reply using your full-sized QWERTY keyboard.

Myplayer
£2.00

Myplayer opens up the Galaxy S III's PopUp Play functionality to all phones and adds a TV catch up-style streaming service into the mix for good measure. In doing so, Myplayer also manages to pull off some of the best streaming we've seen as well as a simple user interface.

Netflix
Free with subscription

£5.99 a month will get you Netflix on every compatible device you own - Android phones and tabs included. With a clean, simple UI and fantastic video quality, Netflix is the perfect app for any film fan on an unlimited data plan or Wi-Fi connection.

Pocket
Free

Pocket acts as a repository for any websites you send its way, downloading them for offline reading and formatting them perfectly for your smartphone. The application also has web-based plug-ins, so you can even send sites its way when at your PC or Mac.

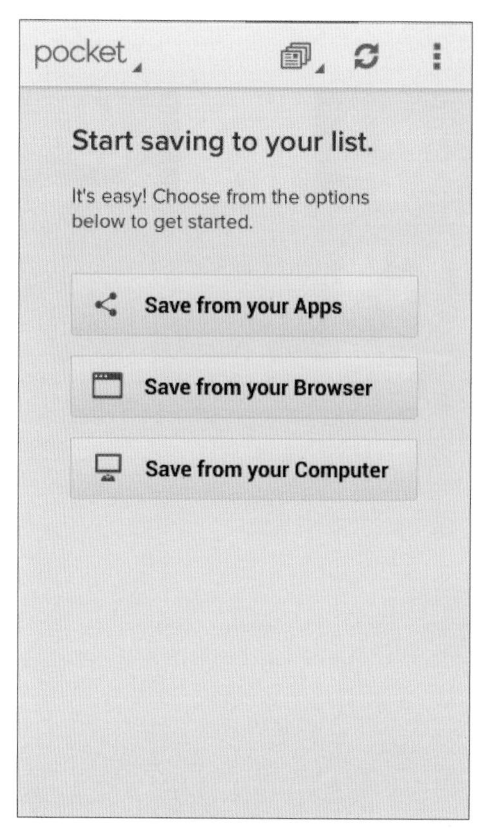

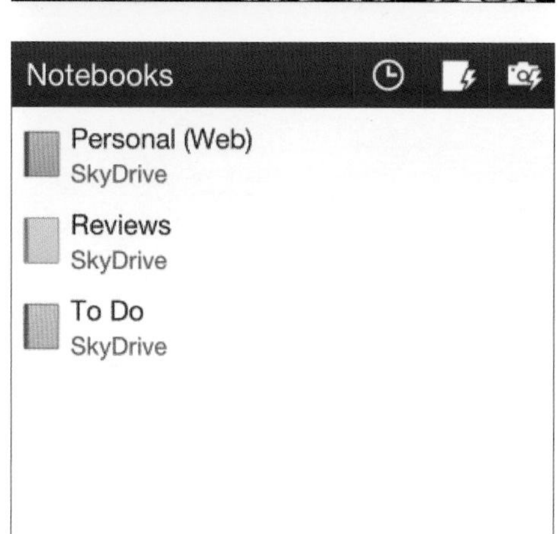

OneNote
Free

If you use the desktop version of One Note you'll know it's perfect for students, with notebooks and section breaks aplenty. While less comprehensive than its desktop counterpart, the Android app is free and lets you edit and view files on the fly.

Pinterest
Free

While many thought this picture-centric social network would fall as quickly as it rose, in the realms of fashion, baking and pets, it's still going strong. The Pinterest app enables you to create pins, manage your profile and repin on the go with little more than a few swipes and a tap.

Pocket Cast

£1.99

Pocket Cast is arguably the best podcast app for audio and video podcast management. Downloading your subscribed casts to your phone, the app is quick and easy to set up and even auto-deletes old podcasts when they've been listened to or expired.

QuickPic

Free

If you're looking for a less busy alternative to Samsung's comprehensive gallery, look no further than QuickPic. It's a piece of cake to install and can be set to manage your pictures by default. It's also lightning fast to open, making short work of even your highest resolution images.

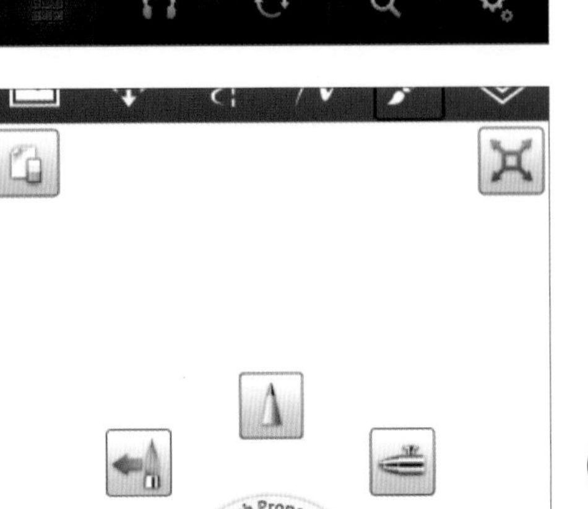

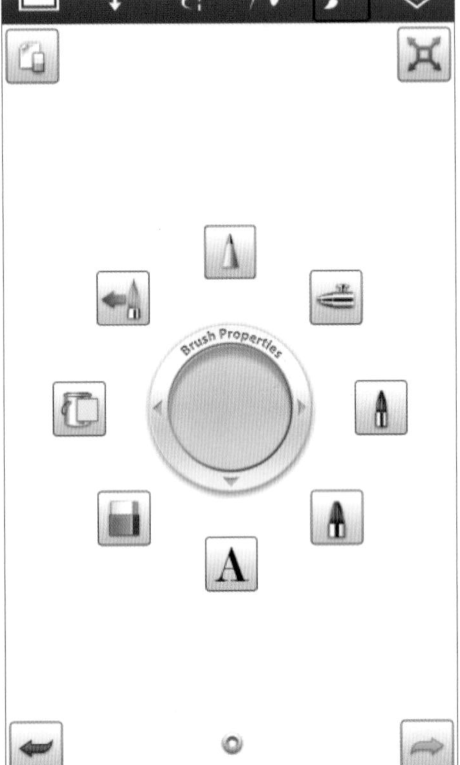

Sketchbook

£1.24

If you're lucky enough to have a Samsung Galaxy Note, Note 2 or Note 10.1 then the Sketchbook app from AutoDesk is the perfect companion to the S Pen. Loaded with brushes, layers, effects and controls galore, it gives you everything you need to make a mobile masterpiece on the go.

Spotify

Free with subscription

Spotify opens you up to a huge amount of music on the go. Typically associated with streaming, the Android app also gives Spotify members the ability to download a huge amounts of music to their handsets, making for easy listening whether you have an active internet connection or not.

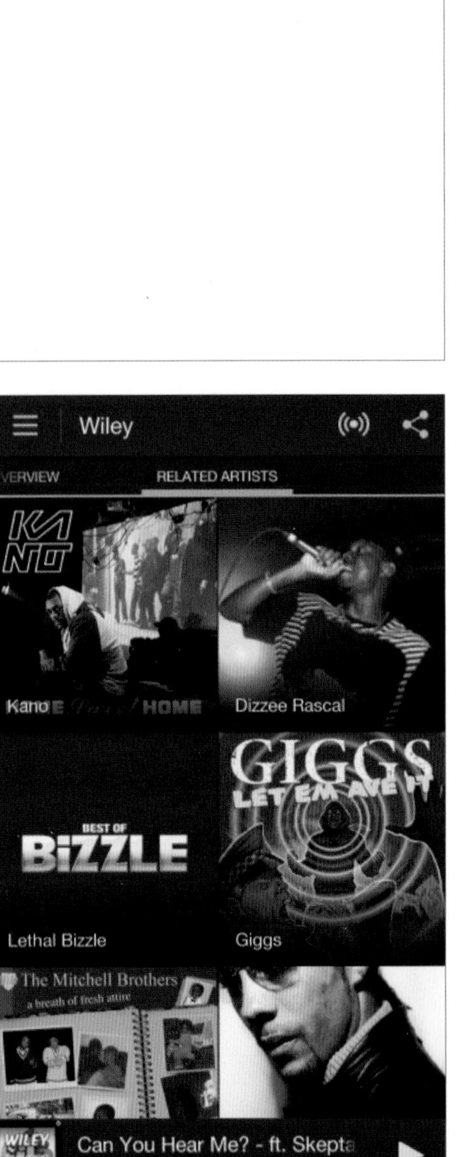

SwitfKey

£2.99

SwiftKey can go one better than keeping up with your typing - it can predict what you're going to type next. The ingenious keyboard links to Facebook, Twitter, Gmail and texts in a bid to learn your writing style, keeping your texts effortless and error free.

Sync SMS

£1.92

Sync SMS is the app to get if you want your phone text messages on your tablet. Just download the application on both devices and follow the syncing instructions. Once done, texts can be enjoyed in full 10.1-inch splendor.

TouchRetouch

£0.62

TouchRetouch is a PhotoShop app in your pocket. Just use it to select a blemished area of any image you take, and it will transform it to match its surroundings. A spot can be gone in seconds, a blemish blasted away or a wrinkle eradicated, earning you brownie points aplenty with even your harshest subjects

Whatsapp

Free

Download Whatsapp and it will instantly scour your phone contacts to find who's else uses the service. Once your Whatsapp contacts list is filled, quickly and easily chat to your contacts and groups, sending them pictures and videos over your data connection saving you precious pennies when compared to MMS.

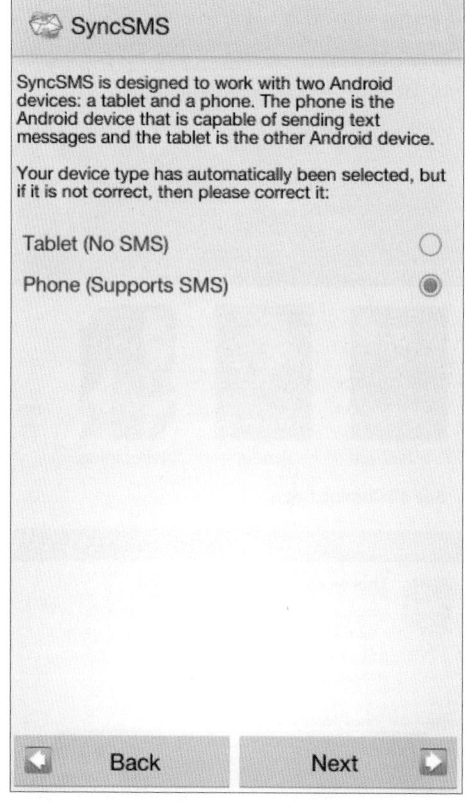

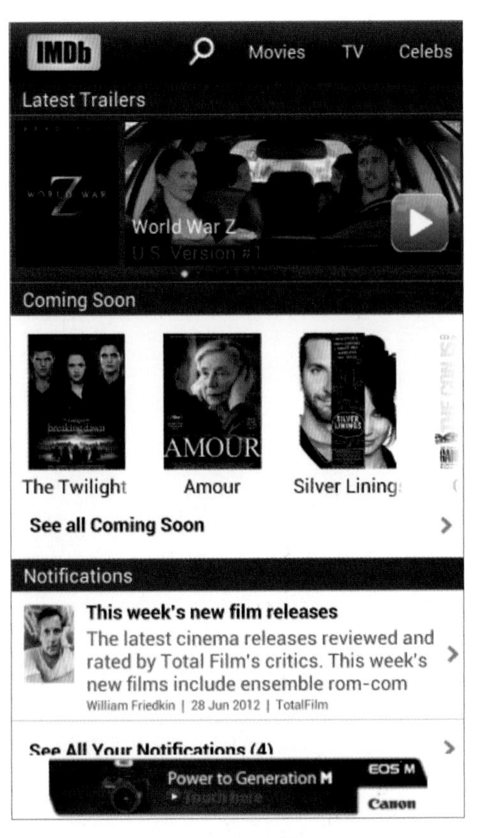

IMDb

Free

Love films? Then you need this application. IMDb is a mammoth movie resource featuring reviews, film listings, actor biographies, and just about everything else you could ever wish to know about films in general. And, best of all, it's available for nothing from Google Play.

Instagram

Free

Take pictures, add effects, and share them with millions of other users. Instagram is the world's most popular social photography application – and with good reason too. Wonderfully designed and free to download, Instagram is a must-have for anyone that enjoys snapping images and sharing them with the world.

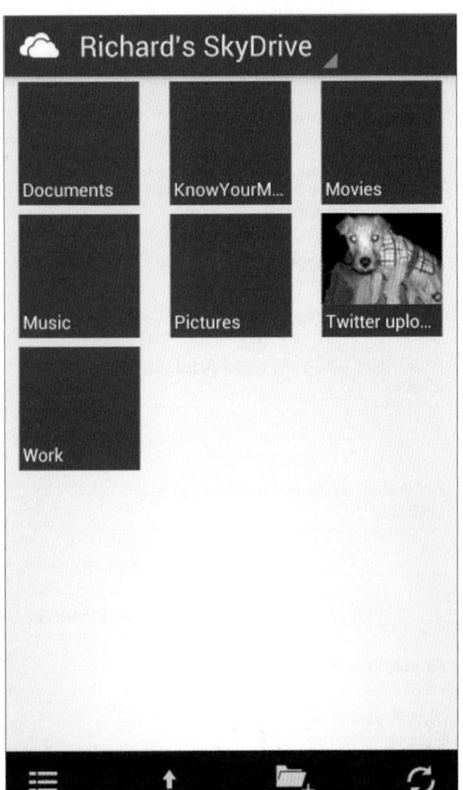

SkyDrive

Free

SkyDrive syncs between your PC and Android handset giving you around-the-clock access to all your most important data and media. The application is free, simple to use, and features tons of added features that ensure you're always connected to your home or work PC wherever you are.

1000+ Ringtones

Free

There are plenty of resources on Google's Play store that'll beef up your handset's selection of ringtones. One such app is 1000+ Ringtones, which is available for free and features all the ringtones you'll ever need – just over 1000, as the name suggests.

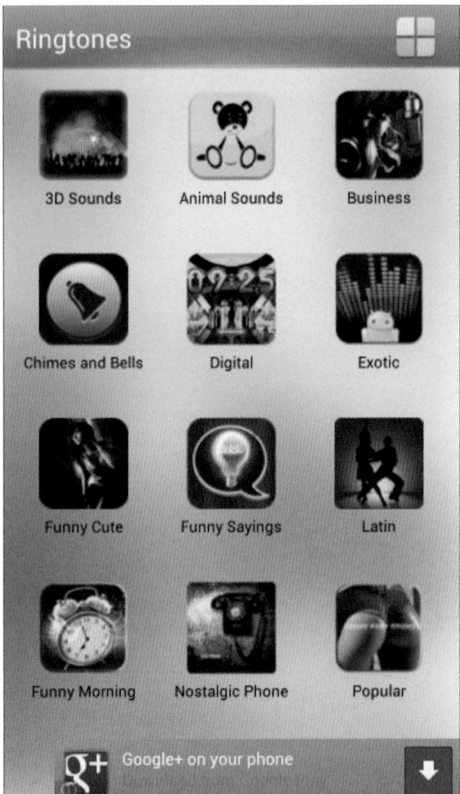

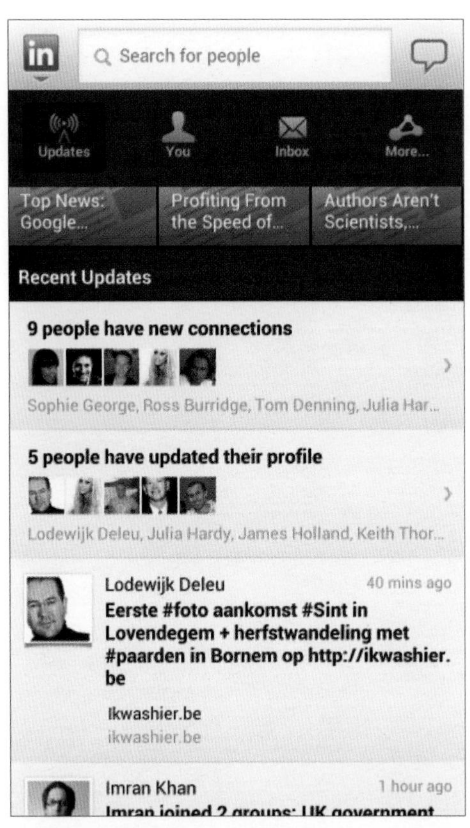

LinkedIn

Free

LinkedIn is the biggest professional social networking site on the planet, and if you're not already registered you are definitely missing out. It's basically Facebook – just for your professional life. Get signed-up, download the free application, and manage your profile from the comfort of your smartphone.

Twitter

Free

As social networks go, they don't come any bigger than Twitter. Millions of users post billions of tweets every week, so why not join in the fun? This app itself is free and features a ton of usual features, so much so that you probably won't use the website ever again!

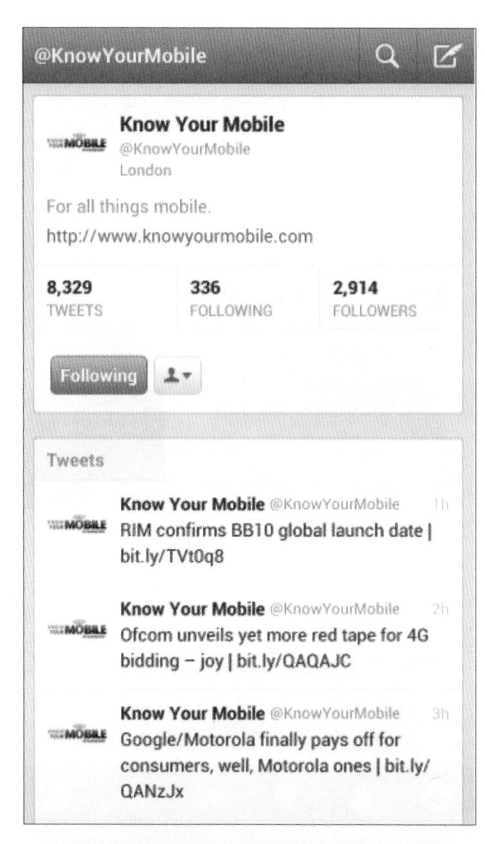

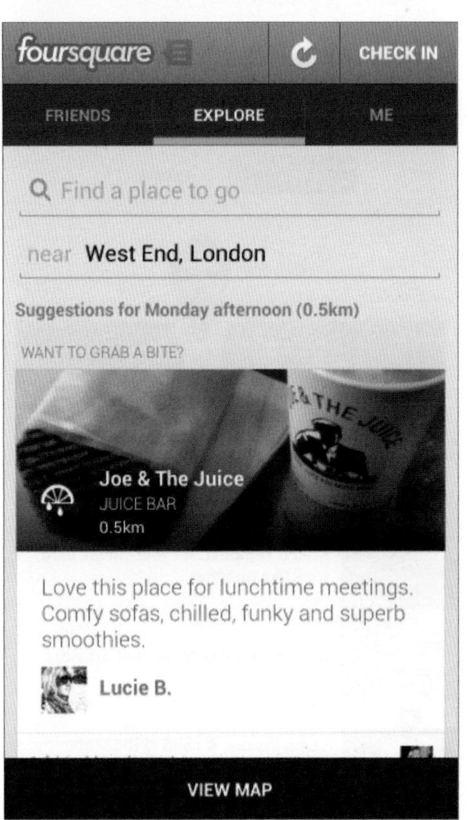

Foursquare

Free

Get to know the world and all of its wonderful places with Foursquare, which now has more than 25 million users. Search for anything – dumplings, Thai food, or free Wi-Fi – and read reviews of bars, restaurants, and businesses. If you love exploring and finding new things, then Foursquare is a must-have app for you.

BBC iPlayer

Free

Take the BBC with you wherever you go with iPlayer, which lets you watch live TV, check listings, catch-up with your favourite shows and episodes, as well as listen to hundreds of BBC Radio shows. It really is a gorgeous-looking application, featuring curated content and recommendations. Best of all, it's free.

StumbleUpon

Free

Explore everything the internet has to offer with StumbleUpon. Simply hit the StumbleUpon button inside this cool free application and you'll be taken to a random website. The app is a must-have for anyone that loves discovering new websites, content, media, and ideas – it's like shuffle for your web browser. And if you're looking for something specific, you can filter results using the app's 500+ interests filter. Simple.

iMediaShare

£3.09

With iMediaShare, you control and stream content from your Android handset to AirPlay-enabled devices, You can also access network-connected devices like a NAS drive and then stream it using AirPlay to a variety of media players.

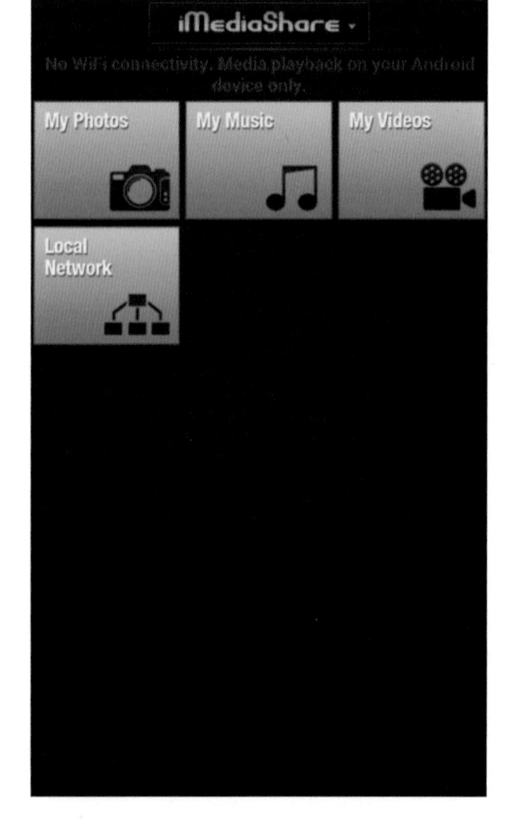

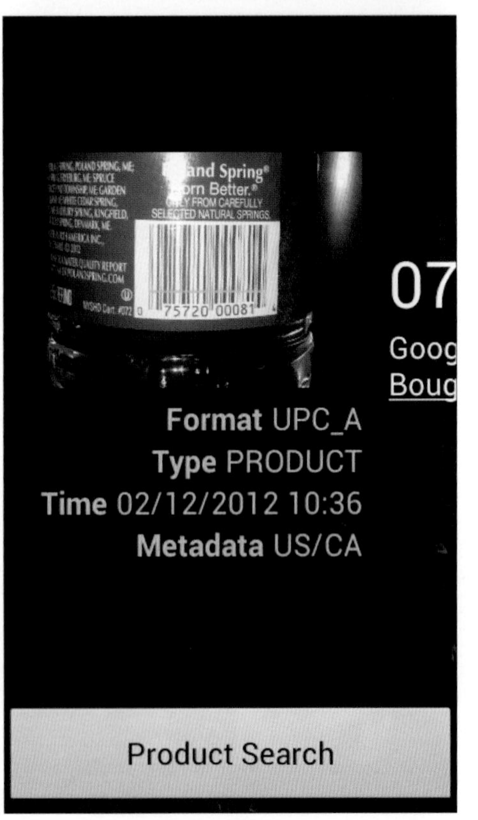

Barcode Scanner

Free

This nifty piece of technology uses your device's camera and scans QR codes and barcodes. It then provides you with information about the product. We're talking pricing, reviews, deals, availability online and the best place to buy it. Barcode Scanner is a must-have application for anyone that shops.

TED

Free

With a wealth of topics and hundreds of thoroughly engaging speakers, there's a talk for everyone inside the TED app. It's a must-have for anyone interested in learning something new. The app itself is free, easy to use, and is constantly updated with new talks. What more could you want?

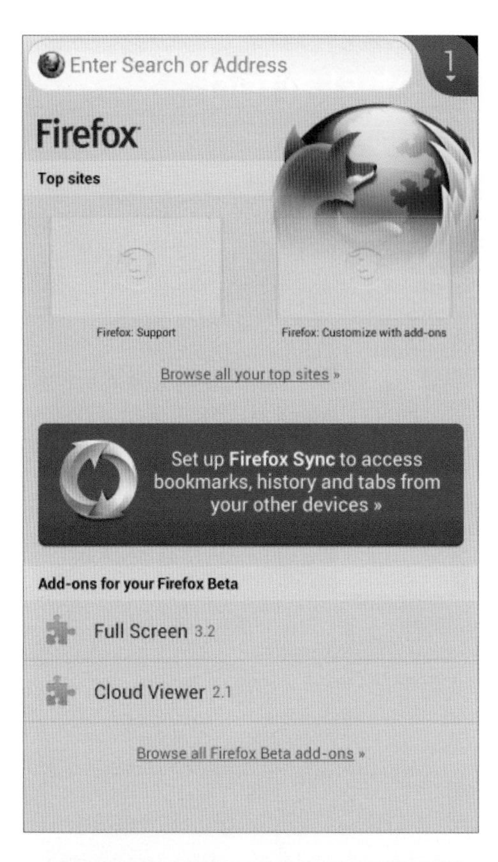

Firefox
Free

Perhaps one of the world's most well-known web browsers, Firefox is now a mainstay on many Android handsets the world-over. Featuring top-notch security features, desktop syncing, and ultra-fast browsing, Firefox is a must-have for any user that does a lot of browsing on their mobile or tablet.

Tumblr
Free

Tumblr is one of the biggest social blogging platforms on the planet, and now it's available on Android. Update, edit, and post content, including pictures and video, straight to your account from the comfort of your smartphone or tablet. If you're serious about blogging you need this application. Oh yeah, it's also free.

Skype
Free

Communicate for free with friends, family and colleagues all over the world with Skype. With its phone call functionality, built-in video call feature, and an IM client, Skype is one of the most polished communication tools available and is therefore a must-have for anyone with friends and family abroad.

Shazam
Free

The science behind Shazam might be complicated, but how it works in practice is simple: open the app, hit the Shazam key, wait a second, and it tells you everything you need to know about a song. As a music discovery tool, Shazam is unparalleled. You need this free application in your life.

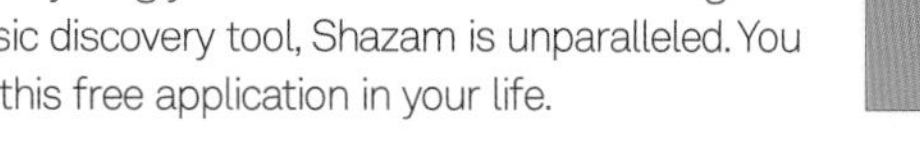

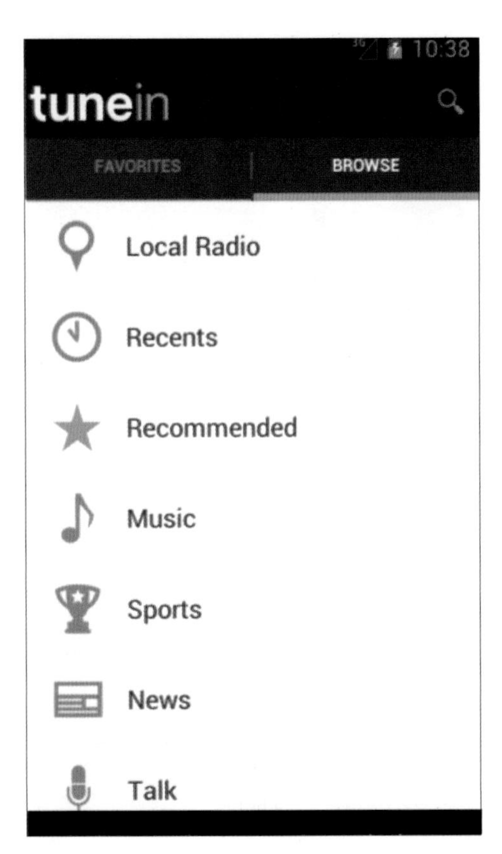

TuneIn Radio

Free

Turn your smartphone or tablet into a DAB radio with TuneIn Radio and get access to thousands of radio stations from all over the world. The application is free, well-designed, easy-to-use, and is packed with tons of cool features like the ability to save your favorite shows and stations.

Xbox SmartGlass

Free

If you own an Xbox then SmartGlass isn't just a must-have app, it's essential. With this free application your Android device will interact with your Xbox 360 in ways you never dreamed possible. SmartGlass is one of the coolest applications ever created, so if you have an Xbox 360 get yourself over to the Play store right now.

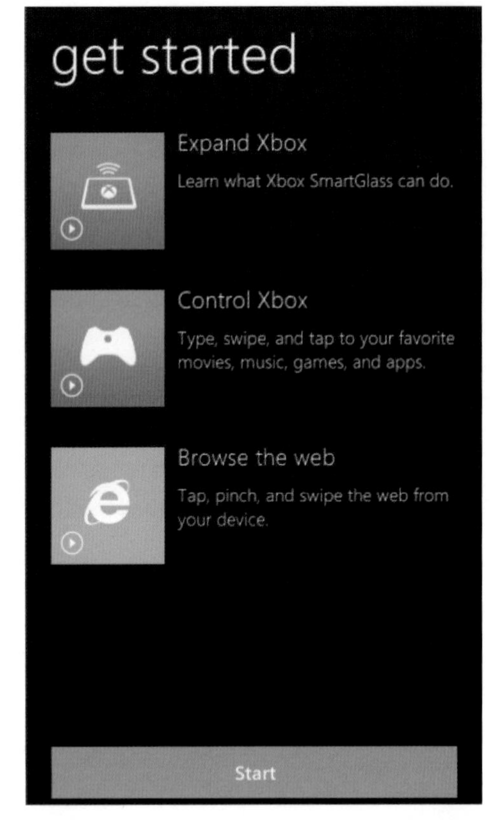

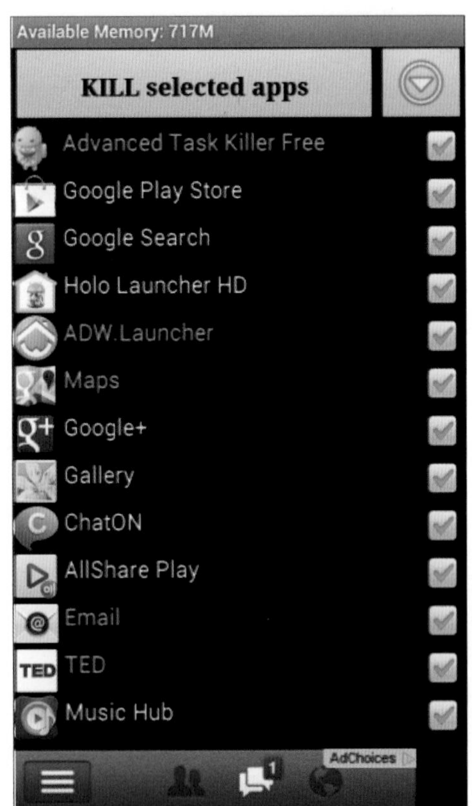

Advanced Task Killer

Free

Multitasking is great on Android but it can inhibit performance if left unchecked. It's also very bad for your battery, too. Advanced Task Killer can kill all running applications, or just the one's you've selected, meaning you no longer have to worry about rogue apps taking up vital memory and battery power.

Wikipedia

Free

Next to Google and Facebook, Wikipedia is one of the most-visited sites on the web. And now you can get all of its encyclopedic-goodness stored on your homescreen for even easier access via the Wikipedia app. It's free from Google Play, simple to use, and more or less exactly the same as the website. Perfect.

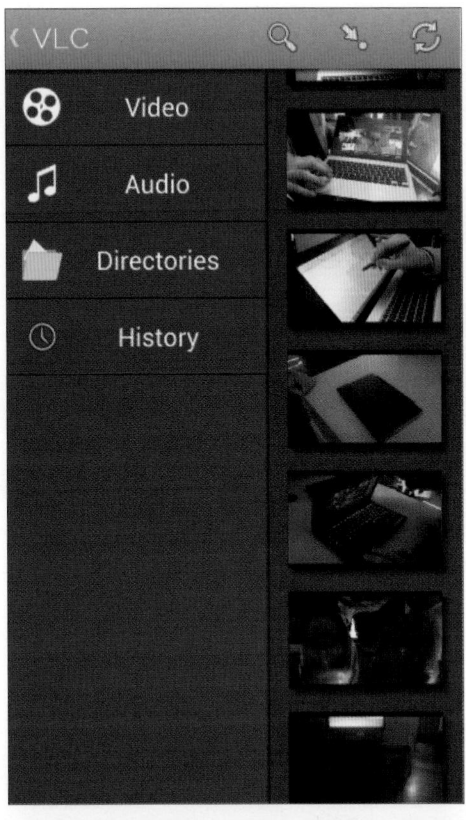

VLC for Android
Free

VLC started life as a media player for PCs and Macs and is famous for supporting pretty much every video codec under the sun. Now in beta on Android, VLC is attempting to do the same for smartphones and tablets. If you watch a lot of video this application is a necessity.

WiFi Analyzer
Free

Want to know how good your Wi-Fi signal is around the house, or find out which channel you're best tuning your home broadband to? Then you need WiFi Analyzer – a free app that provides you with a wealth of information about you're the strength of your home broadband.

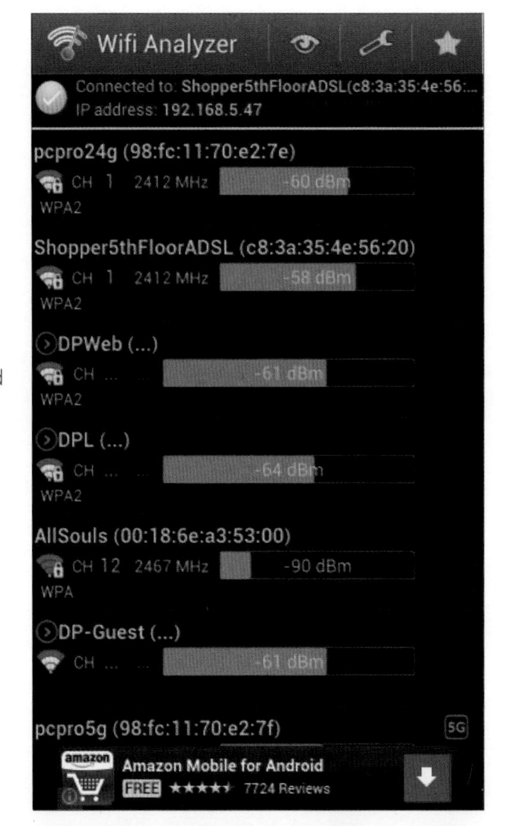

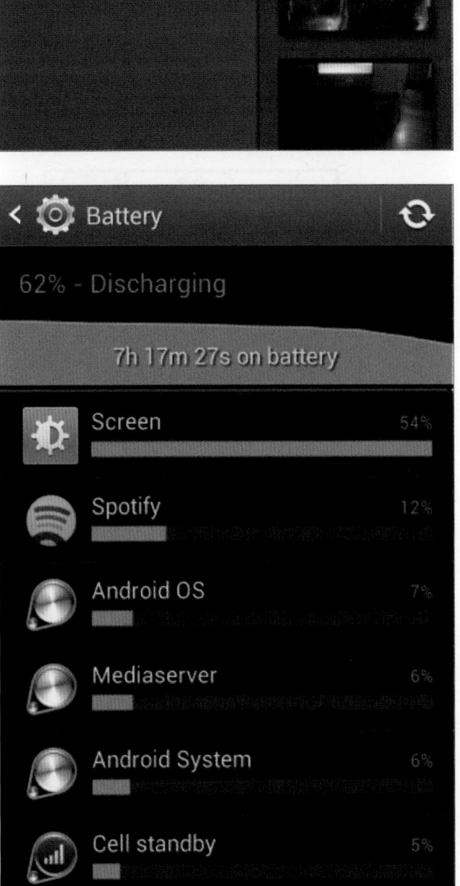

Flipboard
Free

Think of Flipboard as a digital magazine, one that is populated with content and subject matter chosen by you. It's visually stunning, can be placed as a widget on your homescreen, and is always re-populating itself with the latest articles from all over the web.

Battery Saver Pro
Free

Gaming, browsing, tweeting, push email, and listening to music all zap your Android's battery cell. To extend the life of your phone you need a power management tool like Battery Saver Pro. Once activated, it goes to work in the background, and can, in some instances, extend your battery life by 25 per cent.

Developing your own App for Android

You've seen what Google's Play store has to offer, downloaded numerous applications, deleted a few, and discovered new ways of doing things. But have you ever consider building your own Android application?

It's not as hard as you might imagine, and the internet is full of useful resources and guides for developers of all levels. So whether you're a seasoned pro or a complete newbie, there's plenty of help out there to get you moving on your app project.

Our personal favourite is AppMakerStore, which allows you to create and monetise your app. You can even upload the app to the Android Play store for a fee, which will allow anyone around the world to download it.

- To create your app, first head to appsmakerstore.com and set up an account.
- Now you can start creating. First, choose the design you want for your app.
- Now, head to 'Design' and upload a logo and background image if you want one.
- Click on 'Gadgets' to add widgets. These form the meat of your application and AppMakerStore offers the widest selection.

There are loads to choose from, to suit almost every kind of application, including a radio station, shopping catalogue with online purchasing function (you will need to upload your existing shopping catalogue in .csv format), event booking, even live chat and iFrames if you're a seasoned developer and already have the code you need to produce an app, but just need a place to host it.

When you click on a widget, they are added to the list in the centre of the screen. Click 'Save' to see them on the phone screen on the right, and choose the pencil icon below each in the list to edit.

You can click on each of the widget names to change the display name on the app.

Once you've created your app, you can publish it to any app store you wish, including Google Play. Just click on 'Publish Settings' to submit your app. You will need to be registered as a developer on Google Play, which you can do at https://play.google.com/apps/publish/signup

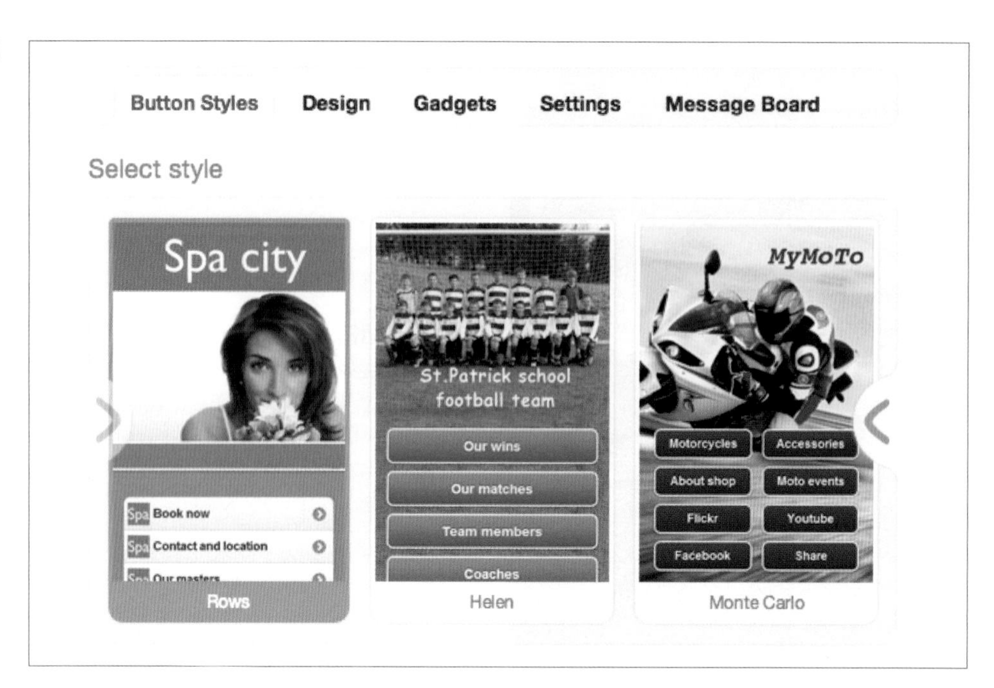

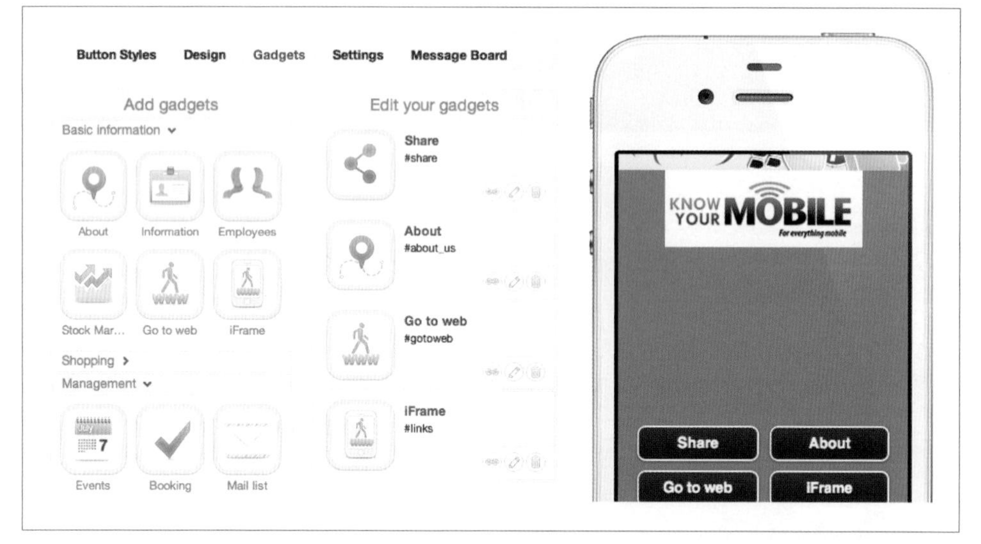

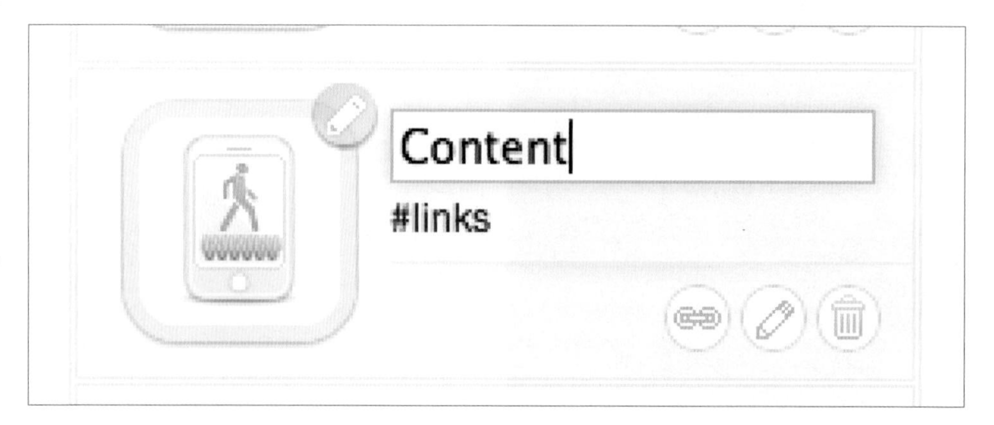

Not convinced by AppMakerStore? Here's a selection of some of the other free resources on the web.

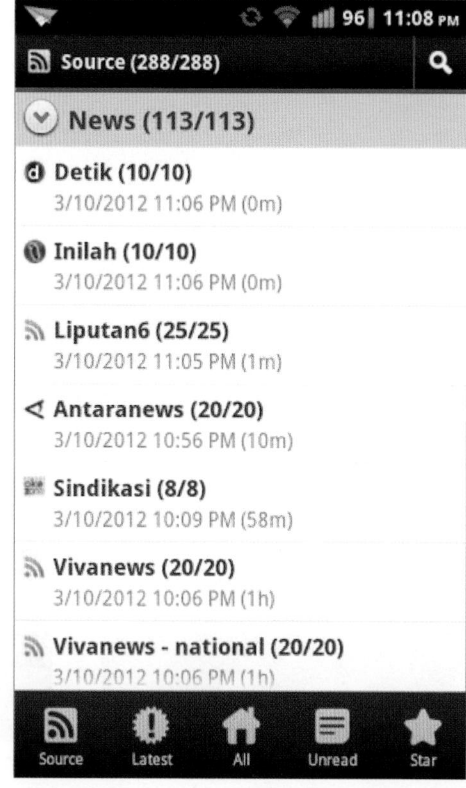

App Yet

Web-based Android application creation tool App Yet is quite a basic offering, but it's great to look at. The basic premise of App Yet is that it turns RSS and Atom feeds into Android applications. Setup and creation is all taken care of online, so you just need to input some data and let App Yet do the rest.

Top Secret Tip

Worried you may go over your data limits? Use the Android Data Usage counter to keep track of your browsing. Head to Settings > Data Usage and you can view how much data you've used, set a limit and monitor how much you're sending and receiving via each of your apps.

AppGeyser.com

Free, simple, and already used by many people the globe over, AppGeyser is one of the most well-known services of its kind on the web. Already have a blog and want to turn it into an application? This could be just what you've been looking for.

The site is simple to navigate around and it shows you exactly how to do everything, starting with the basics: turning your web content into an Android application.

Andromo

Make Android applications without ever using a line of code and upload them to Google Play. The service is free and there's already a community of more than 150,000 developers using it.

Creating your Android application has never been easier, simply design the layout, add the features you want, and Andromo generates all the custom Java code required to make it function correctly. It's that simple and definitely worth a look.

Chapter 5

Photography

Samsung doesn't just make great phones, it also makes great cameras too. We're pretty sure this has something to do with its Galaxy range of smartphones offering some of the best cameraphone credentials around. Coupling fantastic optics, high-resolution sensors, bright LED flashes and Samsung's comprehensive user interface, you'll be amazed as to the quality of shots you can capture on the go with your smartphone.

What better way to pay homage to these fantastic cameras than to explore their inner workings? To kick things off, we'll touch upon Samsung's finger-friendly user interface, telling you what everything on screen means and showing you exactly how to customise your Galaxy camera to suit your sharpshooting needs.

Next, we'll take that knowledge and supplement it with some picture taking tips. Starting with a few pointers specific to the Samsung Galaxy range, then moving onto some timeless rules of photography.

If this all sounds like child's play and you want to get down and dirty with some advanced Samsung Galaxy shooting modes, we cover that too. Found on higher end Samsung Galaxy smartphones, we explain the difference between best face and share shot, HDR and Panorama and help you get to grips with everything you need to get the perfect picture.

But what happens when a picture isn't perfect? No problem, just retouch it using Samsung's own comprehensive Photo Editor. Give your pictures a vintage feel, pixelate a portion of your image or wipe out a pimple or blemish with ease.

If, on the other hand, you're willing to fork out a little extra, we give you an in-depth insight into Photoshop Touch. Packing most of the functions found in Photoshop Elements, and all for £6.99, stick with us if you want to turn your Galaxy shots into on-screen perfection.

The Google Play store also has plenty of other apps that help polish your pics for free or thereabouts. So, what better way to round off the photography guide than a trip through the Google Play store?

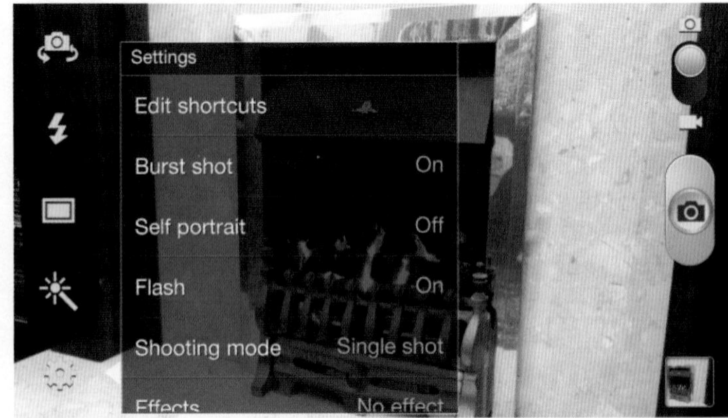

Camera user interface

The user interface (UI) is the camera menu system and it's one of the best things about the Samsung Galaxy range.

We're using the Samsung Galaxy Note 2 user interface as an example. If you have a Galaxy S III, it'll look much the same, however if you have a mid-range model like an Ace 2, you may not have a couple of options we mention.

Starting with an interface map, on the right-hand side are three key elements. At the top-right is a toggle between photo and video shooting. In the centre, there's a shutter release button, below which is a link to the last picture you took and your gallery.

The full screen is your viewfinder and the camera focuses on the area you touch, so in the image above, we tapped the fireplace and that's where the camera focused.

On the left-hand side you'll find five shortcuts stacked on top of one another. From top to bottom, these comprise front/rear camera toggle, flash options, shooting mode, effects menu and settings. The first four options can be customised, while the settings icon is fixed.

To change a shortcut on the left, just long press it and drag it into the grid of icons that will appear to the right.

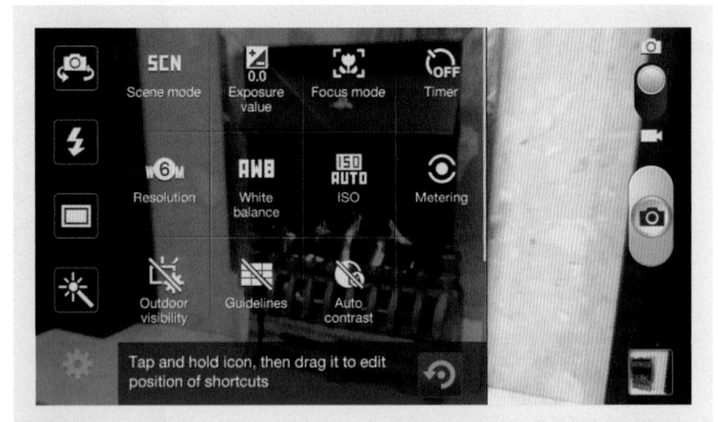

To wrap up our interface guide here's a breakdown of all the shortcuts listed in the above image:

Camera toggle - Toggles between front and rear-facing camera
Flash - Flash on, Flash off or Auto
Shooting mode - Choose from a range of shooting modes from HDR to Panorama
Effect - Select a filter to give your shot some flair
Scene mode - Tell your Galaxy what environment you're shooting in
Exposure value - Changes how dark/light the shot is
Focus mode - Switches between macro, auto and other focus modes
Timer - Takes your shot after a set amount of time
Resolution - Changes the size of your picture
White balance - Compensates for various lighting conditions
ISO - Manually overrides the camera sensor's sensitivity
Metering - Sets how the camera exposes the shot
Outdoor visibility - Ramps up the screen brightness
Guidelines - Lays a 3x3 grid over your viewfinder
Auto contrast - Evens out the contrast of a picture

Take better pictures on your Galaxy

Before we can tell you how to take better pictures on your Samsung Galaxy phone, we'll have to tell you a little bit about photography in general. This way, you'll know why we say what we say and suggest what we do.

Smartphone camera modules are comprised of a sensor and a lens as well as a fair amount of wizardry under the hood. The light passes through the lens, then falls on the sensor, forms an image and appears on the screen thanks to considerable technological wizardry.

The holy trinity of photography: Shutter speed, aperture and ISO
There are three elements that dictate how your pictures turn out, shutter speed, aperture and ISO.

Shutter speed refers to how long the lens is open. The longer the lens is open, the longer the camera sensor is exposed and the brighter the picture. Lots of light is good, though a slow shutter speed can create blurry shots, thanks to handshake and moving subjects.

Aperture refers to how wide open a camera lens is. While compact cameras and SLRs have variable apertures, phones have fixed apertures. The wider the aperture, the more light falls on the sensor and the better the results tend to be. Higher end phones tend to have wider apertures.

ISO is all about sensitivity, more specifically sensor sensitivity. The more sensitive a camera sensor, the shorter the shutter speed. High sensitivity may reduce shutter speed, and therefore hand shake and blur, but in low light especially, it creates considerable image grain, also known as noise.

Our top three Photography tips

Photography tip 1

Rule of thirds

So many camera phone shots you see look a little pedestrian with their centred subjects, skylines and symmetry in spades. When it comes to creating dynamic photographs, symmetry is your enemy. One of the golden rules of photography - the rule of thirds - can help pull you out of a natural inclination to centre everything and into a world of photographs that feel altogether more real.

This rule relies on a 3x3 grid comprised of nine cells. When placed on top of your viewfinder, your focal point should fall on one of the four corners of the centre cell, illustrated in the screenshot below taken on a Samsung Galaxy Note 2. This encourages more considered framing and makes shots look considerably less static and staged.

Photography tip 2

Move, don't zoom

There are two disadvantages to the zoom on your Samsung Galaxy smartphone. The first is the fact that it uses what's known as a digital, not optical zoom. This means rather than having a lens that moves to magnify the image, it simply crops a portion of your picture on the fly. This degrades quality and is irreversible insofar as you cannot uncrop the image.

The second downside to zooming is that it makes us lazy photographers. Sure, there are times when a good old zoom is appropriate, but if you really want to capture a scene in all its glory, get up close and personal and don't be a spectator from a distance. This makes shots look and feel more immersive, totally changing the perspective and getting you more involved.

Photography tip 3

Depth of field

Depth of field is the technical term for what many people call background blur. It enhances a sharp foreground by contrasting it with a soft-focus backdrop. Introducing layers and an expensive look to images, it's commonly associated with high-end cameras. But it's absolutely something you can achieve on your humble smartphone.

All your cameraphone needs is an autofocus lens, which most of the Samsung Galaxy range have. It also only really works on close-up objects. The first step is to jump into the settings and turn on macro focus mode. Next, find your subject, bearing in mind you'll need to get very close to get the maximum depth of field. When framing your shot, make sure there's plenty of depth behind whatever you're shooting. Now tap your focal point and fire. The example here was taken on the Samsung Galaxy Note 2.

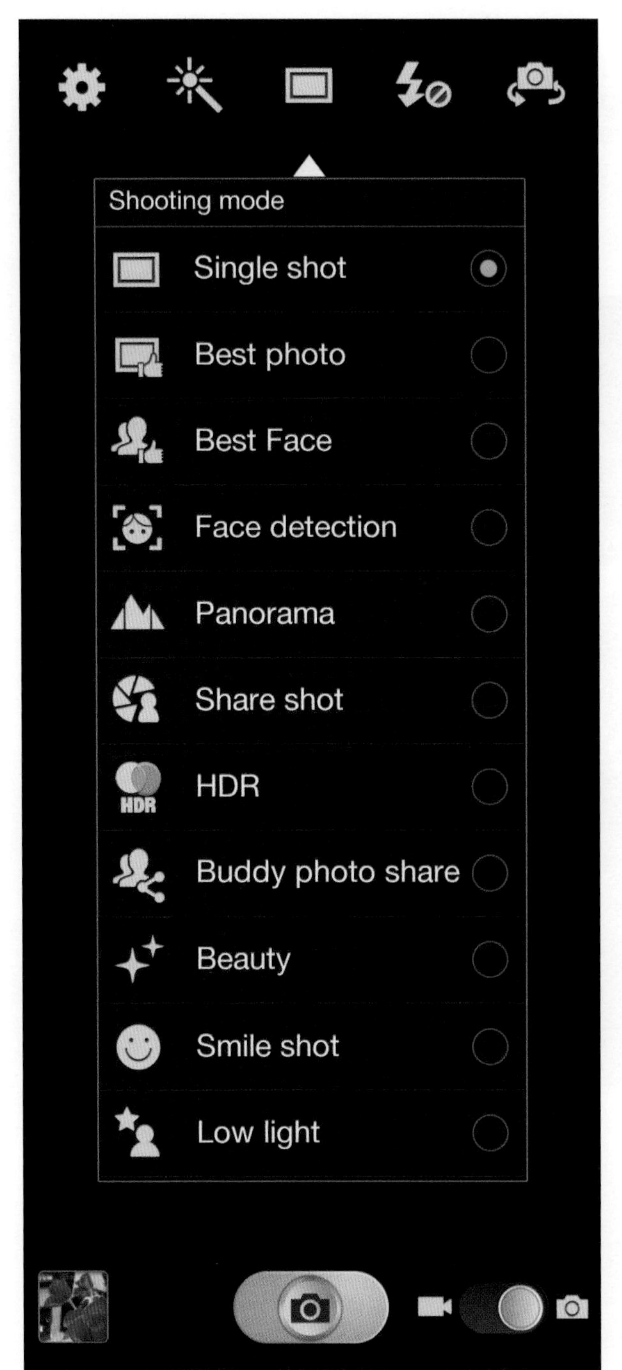

Advanced Galaxy features

If you're wondering what all of the shooting modes on Samsung Galaxy smartphones do, you're in the right place. Not only have we listed all the modes below, we've also provided a bitesize explanation of each. It's worth noting though that these won't be the same on all Galaxy devices.

Best photo: If you're taking shots of a moving object or suffer from a shaky hand, try out Best photo. It takes eight photos one after another in quick succession. The eight photos are displayed side-by-side so you can compare, contrast and choose your best photo.

Best Face: If you're faced with a dreaded group shot, activate Best Face. Your phone's camera will capture multiple photos of your group. Each person's face can then be selected in isolation, mixed and matched from all the photos to create a perfect, albeit digitally fabricated moment.

Face detection: When taking portrait or group shots, turn on face detection for a little help focusing, exposing and colour balancing your picture based on faces detected in-frame.

Panorama: If you want to capture very long photos such as landscapes or interior spaces, turn on panorama. When you take your shot, you'll be prompted to pan left, right, up or down. As you do, your smartphone will stitch multiple pictures together and make one long panorama.

Share shot: Take a picture with Share shot activated and it will automatically send it from your phone to a computer, tablet or another smartphone connected over Wi-Fi direct.

HDR: It stands for high dynamic range and it's perfect if you want to capture a very high contrast scene. As you take a picture, under the scenes the Samsung Galaxy cameraphone captures three shots in quick succession. One is well exposed, one too dark and the last shot too bright. It then lays them on top of one another creating one super shot with a broader tonal range.

Buddy photo share: Back to sharing, only this time with people, not devices. Activate Buddy photo share and take your shot as normal. Your camera phone will detect which of your friend's faces are in the picture of and will ask you whether you want to send the picture to them via email.

Beauty: For those occasions when your subject needs a bit of digital help looking their best, there's Beauty mode. Shoot in this mode to soften focus, even out skin, and add a sparkle to your subject's eye.

Smile shot: If you're one of those people who always misses the smile, activate Smile shot. Able to detect when your subject smiles, it instantly takes the shot automatically - no button press needed.

Adobe Photoshop

There are two versions of Adobe's Photoshop available for your Samsung Galaxy devices. The free version, Photoshop Express, is available across phones and tablets. The paid-for version, Adobe Photoshop Touch, is exclusively available for tablets. We'll start by outlining what you can expect from Photoshop Express, then tell you why - if you have an Android tablet - you might want to opt for the paid version.

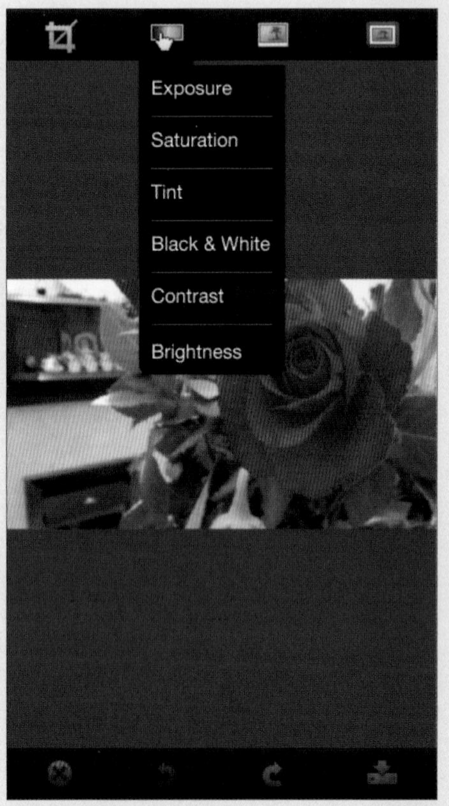

Adobe Photoshop Express
Good for basic photo editing, Adobe Photoshop Express can be downloaded from the Google Play store.

Starting up the application takes you straight to a grid of your images. You begin by choosing the one you want to edit.

Once you've decided, tap it to maximise it then press the menu button on your Galaxy device. Here you can select the 'Edit Photo' option.

The next menu is where the magic happens. At the top, you'll find editing options. The first looks like a set square and gives you the option to crop, straighten, rotate or flip your picture.

The second set of options are all your image adjustments relating to brightness and colour correction. Here you can tweak saturation, contrast and exposure, not to mention give your picture the black and white treatment.

The third option enables you to set a soft focus blanket across your entire image. This is particularly useful for beauty shots, evening out skin imperfections and blemishes.

The final option in Photoshop Express is where you can add all your Instagram-esque filters and borders.

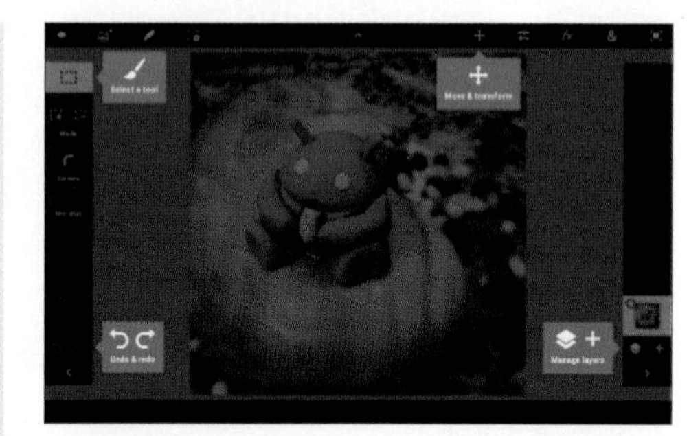

Adobe Photoshop Touch
If all that seemed a tad superficial, then you'll want some Photoshop Touch in your life. As mentioned, it's only available for tablets, but it really is considerably more advanced than Photoshop Express. In fact, we'd go so far as to say that it virtually matched Photoshop Elements - a considerably more expensive package with support for selection tools, brushes, layers and levels to name a few.

While all these advanced options sound overwhelming, there are also comprehensive tutorials which walk you through every part of the app, making the £6.99 asking price great value for money.

Top Secret Tip

If you have the lock screen pattern set up on your Samsung Galaxy device, you're obviously taking security seriously. What happens if you forget the pattern though? When you set up a lock pattern, you'll be asked to enter a PIN. If you're prone to forgetting that too, you can choose Face unlock, Password or Face and voice instead.

Top photography apps

- Photaf Panorama
- Instagram
- Lomo Camera
- HDR Camera+
- Quickpic

Samsung Photo Editor

For anyone who hasn't ventured into the Samsung Apps world just yet, Samsung's Photo Editor is one app highlight you definitely don't want to miss. It's an incredibly comprehensive, free app that lets you transform your mobile photographs with little more than a tap and a swipe. First thing you've got to do is download it though, so get to it. Once you've installed the app and it's loaded up, choose a picture to edit, then select one of four options:

Option 1 Transform

The first is the simplest option and could well suffice for any basic editors out there. If you want to resize, rotate or crop your pictures, this is where you want to be. In addition to being simple and intuitive, it's comprehensive with options to flip images and resize them in multiple ways.

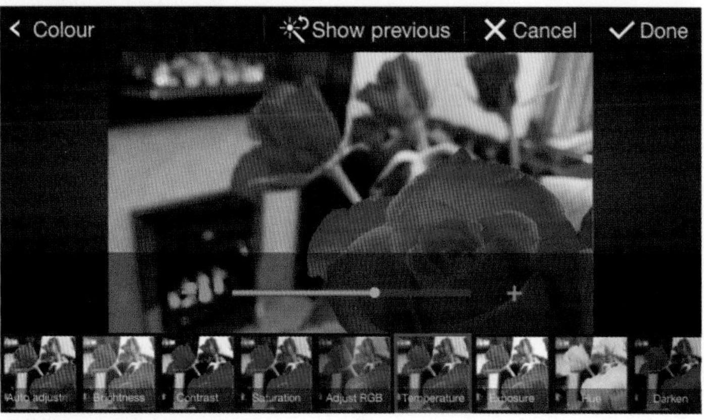

Option 2 Colour

The second option, colour, is the road to go down if you fancy playing with hue and saturation. You can also tweak elements like brightness, contrast and exposure here too, making it very useful for simple adjustments as well some drastic recolouring.

Option 3 Effects

Primarily providing a range of filters you can apply to your photo, there's more to be found if you dig a little deeper into the menu. The filters range from an Instagram-style vintage filter through to an off-the-wall pop art filter and, our favourite, a halftone filter. If you want to get more involved, the advanced effects panel opens you up to red eye removal as well as filters you can paint on such as pixelate and colour accent. The best filter - in our opinion - is spot healing, cleaning up marks and blemishes in no time flat.

Option 4 Decoration

The final option in our arsenal of image adjusters is decoration and, boy, is it multifaceted. You can apply frames to your photos, some classical, some fun, all free. Next up, you have the option to add digital stickers to your pictures Multi-Grid is the penultimate decoration option, collating multiple pictures into one clean, attractive grid that you can manipulate extensively. Finally, decoration presents you with an option where you can draw or write all over your pictures with your finger or S Pen, depending on which Galaxy handset you own.

Chapter 6

Music & Multimedia

Overview

Music

In this section we'll be looking at music and how it's accessed, uploaded and experienced on your Samsung Galaxy device. Nobody uses MP3 players anymore – everything's now done on your phone. Here, we will show you everything you need to know about music and your Galaxy smartphone.

Every handset – be it an iPhone, BlackBerry or Android device – comes equipped with a bespoke music player. On a Samsung device you don't just get its Music Player – you get Samsung's Music Hub as well, which is a marketplace for buying and downloading tracks and albums.

Uploading tracks and albums to your device is simple. Just plug it into your PC via USB to copy tracks over or search for connected drives, NAS storage, for instance, and download tracks over the air (OTA).

Once tracks are loaded, you're good to go. You can even setup a Music Player widget on one of your homescreens for even easier access to your library of tracks.

The Music Player: Adding and managing music, playlists and more

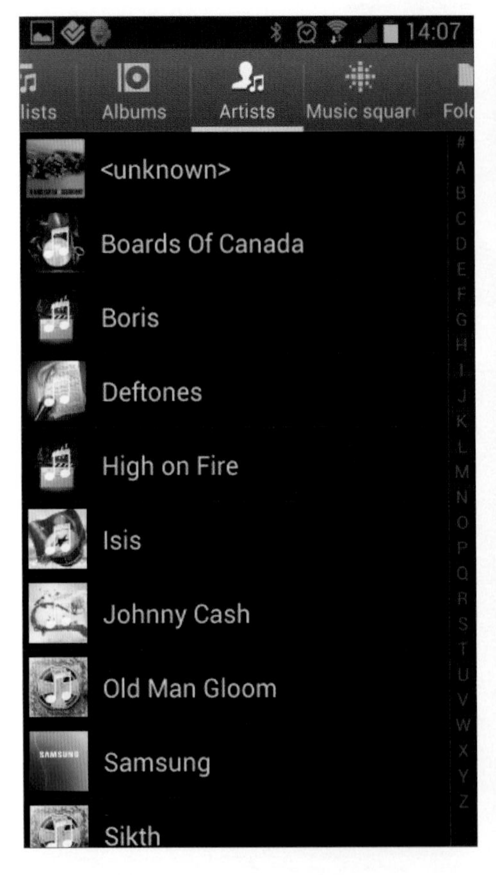

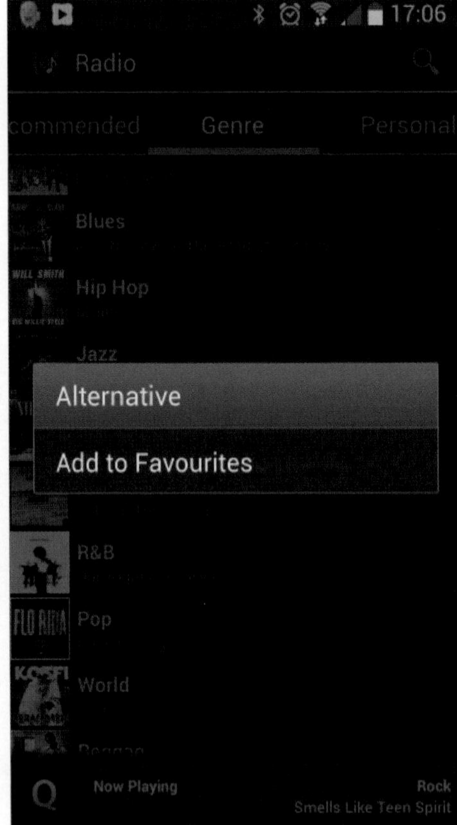

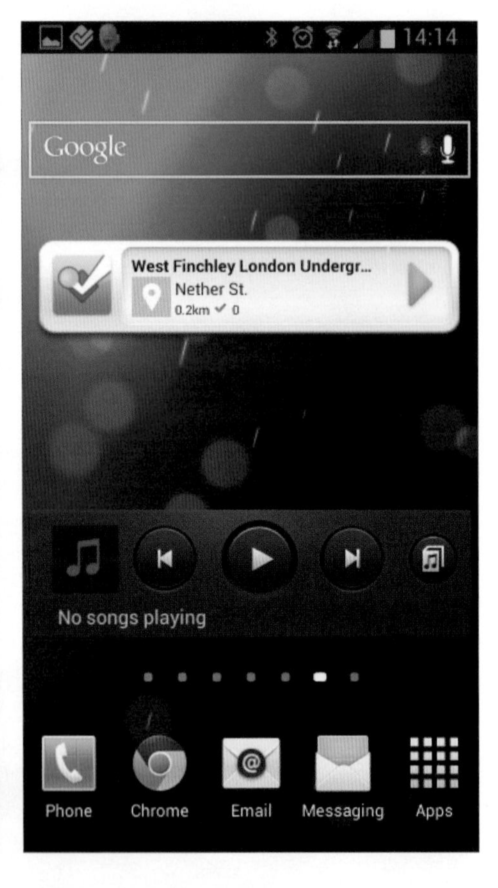

Adding music

Getting music onto your Galaxy device is extremely simple – everything you need, including the USB cable for connecting it to your PC, is provided inside the device's box.

All Samsung devices support a myriad of music file types, including: non-DRM ACC, AAC+, eAAC+, MP3, WMA, 3GP, MP4, and M4A. You may use a variety of media players on your PC – most people have Windows Media Player and iTunes – but as long as your music files are stored in a folder on your computer it doesn't matter.

> **Top Secret Tip**
> Quickly uninstall apps you don't want any longer by long pressing them from the Apps Drawer and dragging them to the recycle bin icon in the top right-hand corner of the screen.

Below we'll show you how to transfer music from your Windows-powered PC or OS X-based Apple Mac to a smartphone or tablet using the USB cable.

- Once the PC recognises it, select Settings > Wireless and network > USB utilities
- Select the 'Connect storage to PC 'option
- Connect your Galaxy device to your PC via the cable
- On the device's screen, select the 'Connect USB storage' option
- A removable disk mount will now appear on your computer. It'll be listed under 'Computer' on Windows and on the 'Desktop' if you're using a Mac
- Open the folder and drag and drop music into it.
- You might want to create a sub-folder inside, entitled music, in order to keep things nice and tidy.

Transferring via iTunes

You can move music directly from your iTunes library with any Galaxy-branded device. Once the device is connected to your PC – as described here – simply drag files over from iTunes into the disk mount folder.

Transferring via Windows Media Player

You can also move music over to your device using Microsoft's Windows Media Player. Here it's done via Windows Media Player's Sync tab.

- Select the 'Sync' tab inside Windows Media Player
- Drag over the songs you want to sync
- Hit 'Start Sync' and Windows Media Player will start transferring the music over to your phone

Once everything has completed and your device is packed full of music, simply tap the 'Disconnect Storage from PC' option on the device. Wait a moment and then disconnect the USB cable.

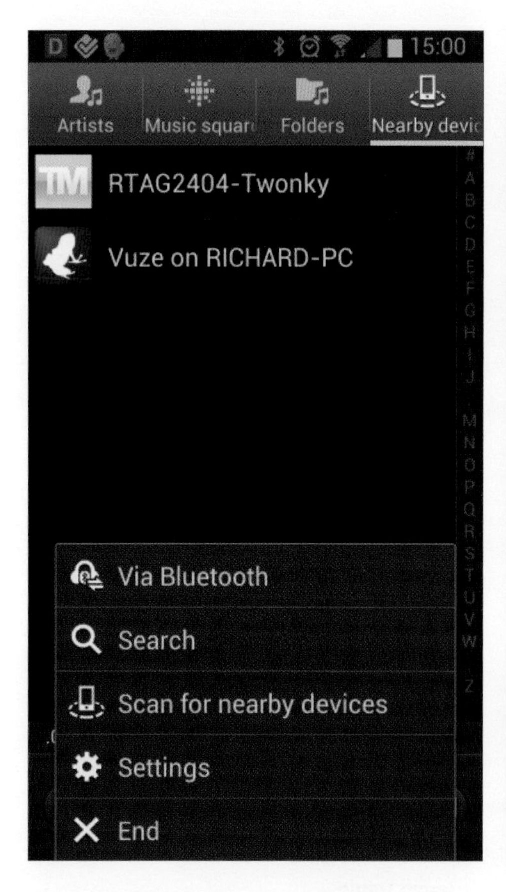

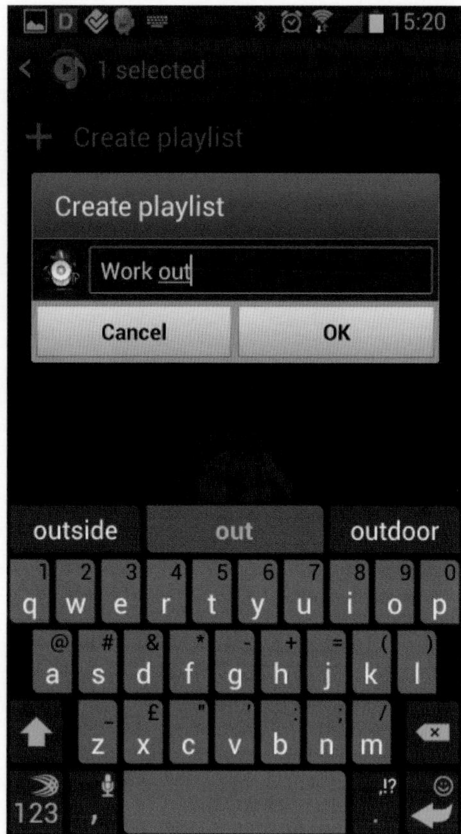

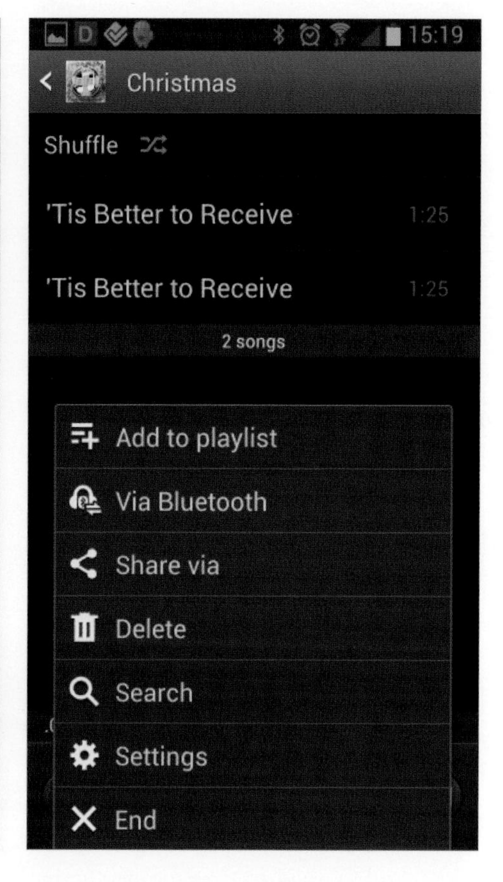

Connecting to devices wirelessly

Samsung's Music Player will also connect to storage devices and PCs that are logged onto the same wireless network. That means if you have a Network Attached Storage (NAS) drive in your home, you can transfer music over to your smartphone or tablet wirelessly.

Here's how it's done:

- Open the Music Player
- Scroll left to right across the top menus until you see 'Nearby devices'
- Select this,and wait a moment
- All supported network-attached devices should now appear
- Select one to view its contents
- Once inside, hit the 'Menu' key and select the 'Download' option
- Now, choose the tracks you want to download – please note: you can only download 100 tracks at a time
- Once you've selected the tracks you want, hit 'Done' and they'll start downloading

Managing music

Once you have all your tracks stored on your device, Samsung's Music Player takes care of everything else sorting them in order of artist, album and track name.

However, it's probably worth ensuring that all your music is organised into the correct albums and track names prior to moving it over to your smartphone. Make sure everything is labelled properly and stored in the correct folder or album.

Browsing music

Open the Music Player application and you're presented with several options for viewing content: All, Playlists, Albums, Artists, Music Square, Folders, and Nearby devices.

Looking for a specific album? Select the album category and scroll down until you find it. Perhaps you want a certain song? In that case, select 'All' and scroll until you find it. And if you're after a certain artist, select the 'Artist' tab and find them that way.

Creating a playlist

Making playlists with the Music Player is simple. The hardest part will be deciding what tracks to include – but we can't help you with that, we're afraid. Playlists are great for parties, workouts at the gym, or aiding concentration when working. Here we'll show you how to build one:

- Locate the track you want, either via the All, Artist, or Albums tabs
- Open the song and hit the 'Menu' key
- You'll be presented with several options. Select 'Add to playlist'
- Now you'll be prompted to create a playlist
- Tap the '+' symbol to create a name for your playlist
- Select 'OK' and you have a playlist
- Now you can peruse your music and add tracks to that list
- You can create as many playlists as you like

Create your own radio station with Music Hub

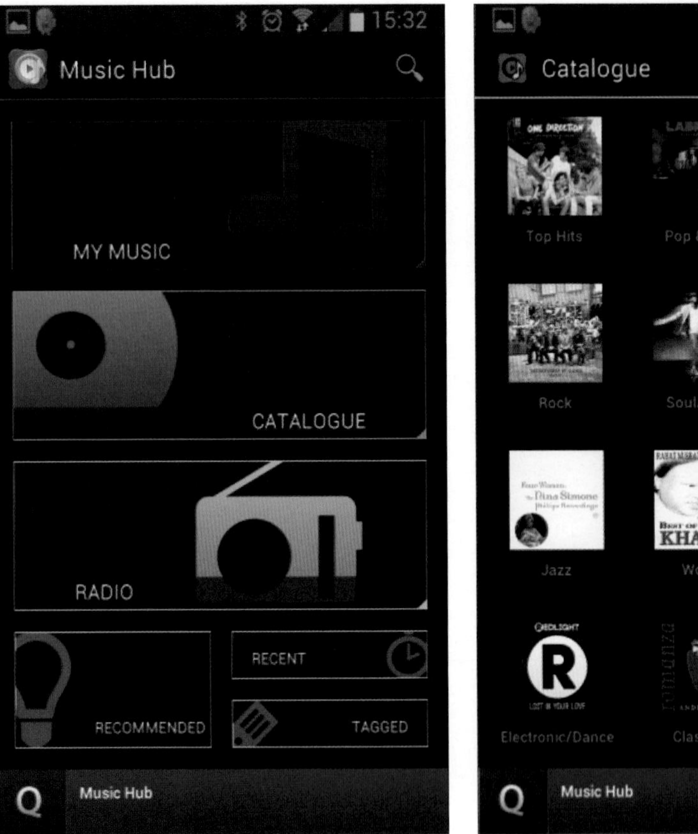

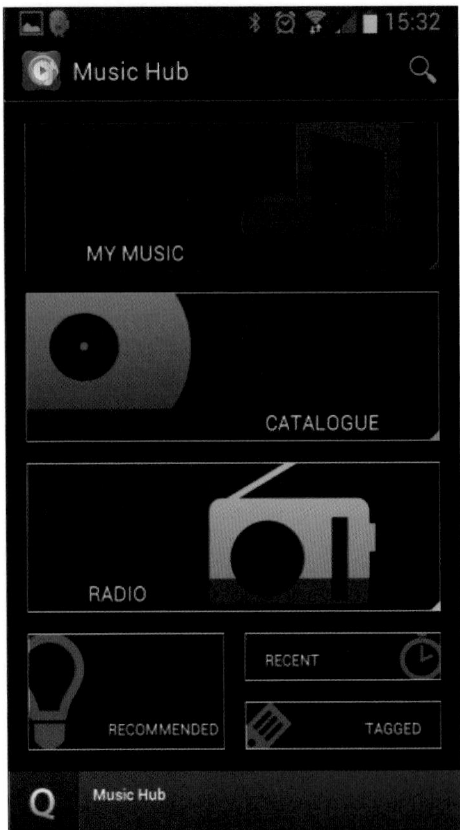

With Music Hub, Samsung has taken the best parts of iTunes, Pandora, and Spotify and rolled them into one service. Here you can do everything, from streaming music, purchasing and downloading tracks, listening to radio stations or creating your own.

To access the service you will need a registered Samsung account or be willing to set one up as soon as you open Music Hub.

Then, just follow the on-screen steps – it only takes a minute.

Top Secret Tip

App keeps crashing? You can easily force quit it by pressing and holding the app from the multitasking menu (just press and hold the home key), press and hold the app icon, select App info and then force stop. You can also see from here how much storage the app is using and permissions.

Once logged in you will be able to browse millions of tracks and stream them to your Galaxy device. If you want to discover something new, check out the 'Radio' feature inside Music Hub where thousands of tracks are collated into stations for your listening pleasure.

You can even create your own personal radio station based on the artists you love. To do this, all you need to do is flag tracks and artists you like by tagging them and Music Hub will build up a list of recommendations, which becomes your personal radio station.

You can even use your personal collection of tracks, the ones that you've synced over from your PC, to search for similar artists inside the Music Hub. To do this, simply tap the drop-down icon and select 'Find similar music.' Music Hub will then trawl its 19 million songs to locate new artists that are similar to ones you already know and love.

Best radio apps

With an Android device, you're not just limited to onboard native applications. You can also browse Google's Play store for additional radio applications.

Many are free, sport excellent features, and are an indispensable tool for discovering new music and keeping up to date with current events.

Here's a selection of some of the best:

TuneIn Radio
The biggest and best of all free radio applications for Android and iOS, TuneIn Radio, has more features that your standard DAB radio. It should be your first port of call for all your radio-based requirements

Stitcher Radio
With more than 10,000 radio shows, podcasts, and live stations, Stitcher Radio is one hell of an app. It's laid out beautifully, is easy to use, and even lets you browse and listen to podcasts.

Jango Radio
Enter the name of your favourite band or artist and Jango Radio will create a personalised radio station just for you based solely on the artists you like. Similar to Pandora and just as easy to use, Jango is one of the best ways to discover new music. Best of all, it's free.

Mobile Radio Live
Mobile Radio Live brings thousands of radio stations and shows from around the world to your mobile. Sports, politics, music, talk-radio, and film are all covered. It's a great app and you can even browse stations by country - handy if you're looking for something specific.

Overview

Video

Like music, video is an integral part of any smartphone and tablet experience. On a Samsung device, in addition to market-leading display technology, so videos look truly stunning, you also have tons of cool features for capturing, viewing and sharing content to and from your device.

There are core applications such as YouTube for video clips and video-on-demand services like Netflix and LoveFilm for a more refined experience. Not enough? No problem. There's also iPlayer, 4OD, and Google's Play store for everything else.

In this chapter we'll look at how you get videos – films and TV shows – onto your device, as well as how you share them with connected devices like Smart TVs, using tools like AllShare and Twonky.

Using video: Adding TV/video to your phone

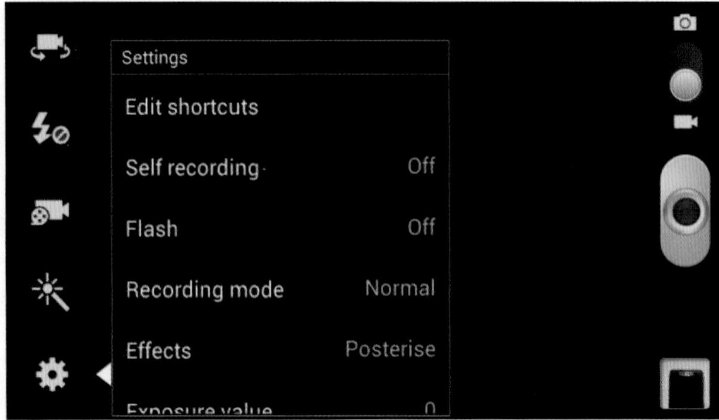

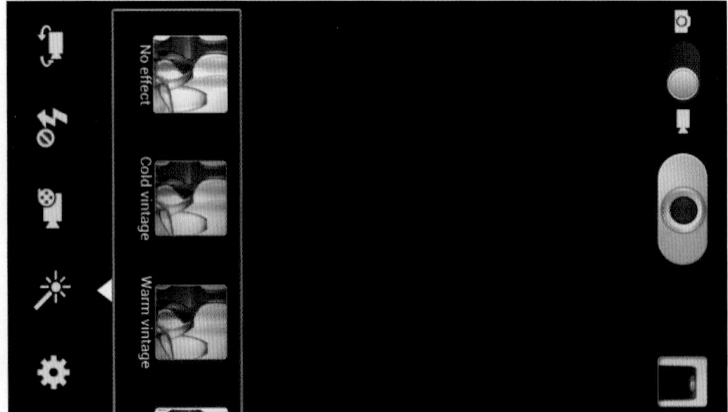

It's worth adding a selection of films and TV shows onto your device for when you're away from an internet connection – such as when you fly or travel on the tube.

Here's how to transfer videos from your PC to your smartphone or tablet:

- Attach your Galaxy device to your PC with the USB cable
- If you are using a PC you may have to install some software. Do this when prompted and then continue
- On your phone/tablet, pull down the notification bar and tap 'USB Connected'
- A notification should appear, select 'Mount' and your device will enter USB Storage Mode
- An icon should appear on your desktop – this is your phone in USB Storage Mode
- Now, just drag-and-drop files into the folder like as you did when transferring music
- That's it! Once the films and TV shows have downloaded successfully, safely remove your phone from USB Storage Mode and disconnect.

All your videos will be stored in the Video Player application. From here you can share them in a variety of locations including Facebook, Dropbox, Drive, Google+, email and Evernote.

You can also download videos from connected devices like Network Attached Devices (NAS), which can sometimes be quicker and less hassle than using wires. Of course, this all depends on the speed of your home's Wi-Fi connection.

To do this: open up the Video Player application, select the 'Nearby Devices' tab, choose the one you'd like to explore, locate the film/TV show you want and download it.

Capturing video

Let's take a brief look at capturing HD video using your Galaxy device. All captured video footage is stored inside the Video Player application.

How to film HD video

- Open the camera application and switch to video mode. Along the left should be a selection of options: 'Settings', 'Effects', 'Recording Mode', 'Flash,' and, finally, a toggle for switching to portrait mode
- You can add effects using the 'Effects' icon. It's similar to how Instagram works. Try out different types of effects and tones, see what you like, and experiment until you find something that works
- Thinking of sharing a video online? You might want to limit the quality so it uploads quicker. To do this tap the 'Recording Mode' option and select one of the four options: 'Normal', 'Limit for MMS,' 'Slow Motion' and 'Fast Motion'
- To view a video, click the icon at the bottom right of the display and you'll be taken to the Gallery application where you can view all your images and videos.

Sharing video

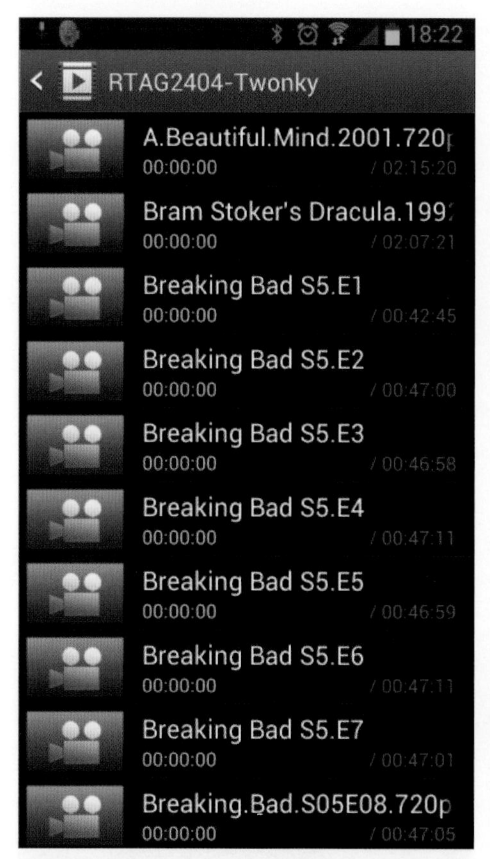

Twonky is a fast and easy way to connect your PC, HD TV, PlayStation/Xbox 360, Apple TV, and smartphone. The application is free and, once installed, shows up as a sharing option within most applications, including the Gallery.

Twonky, like AirPlay, is essentially wireless streaming and because it's supported by thousands of devices it's an excellent solution for all of your home-based file streaming needs. We can't recommend it highly enough.

Top Secret Tip

Want to scrap the lockscreen? Although it will leave your phone open to all sorts of security nightmares, it makes your phone a lot easier to access. Just head to Settings > Screen lock and select none. Voila! You'll now be able to access your phone instantly by tapping the power button.

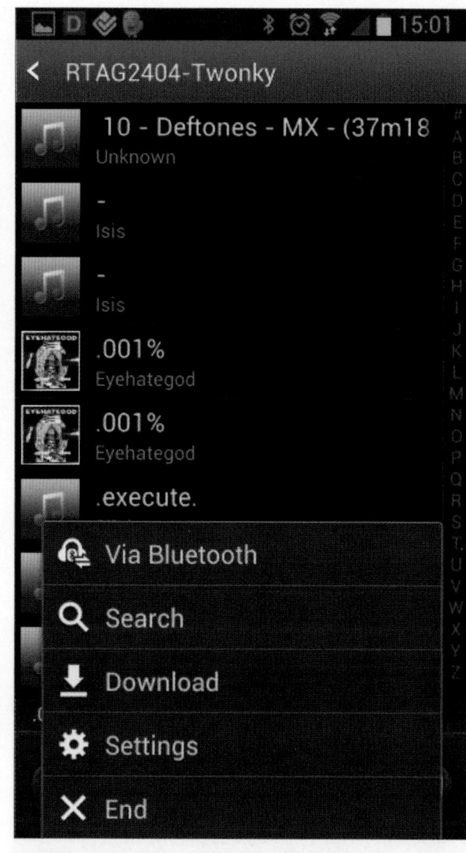

Sharing video from phone to HD TV

- Make sure your HD TV is turned on and is connected to a Twonky-supported device
- Open the Gallery application
- Go to 'Videos,' hit 'Menu' and select the video you want to share
- Once selected, tap the sharing icon and select Twonky
- Twonky will now stream the video from your phone to your HD TV

To share the video elsewhere, such as to Dropbox or Google Drive, just select that option instead. The more applications you download, the more sharing options you'll have.

Top Secret Tip

Samsung Galaxy devices feature a number of photography features, whatever the operating system version number.

One of these extra features is Share Shot, which enables you to quickly share shots with nearby Samsung users in real time.

When you're in the Camera app, tap on the shooting mode button (in the middle) and then scroll down and check Share Shot.

If other friends are also using a Samsung Galaxy device, get them to activate the feature too.

You'll also need to tun Wi-Fi Direct on. To do this, navigate to Settings > Wi-Fi > Wi-Fi Direct.

As long as you're all within 100 metres of each other, shared images will be stored in a Share Shot album on the device.

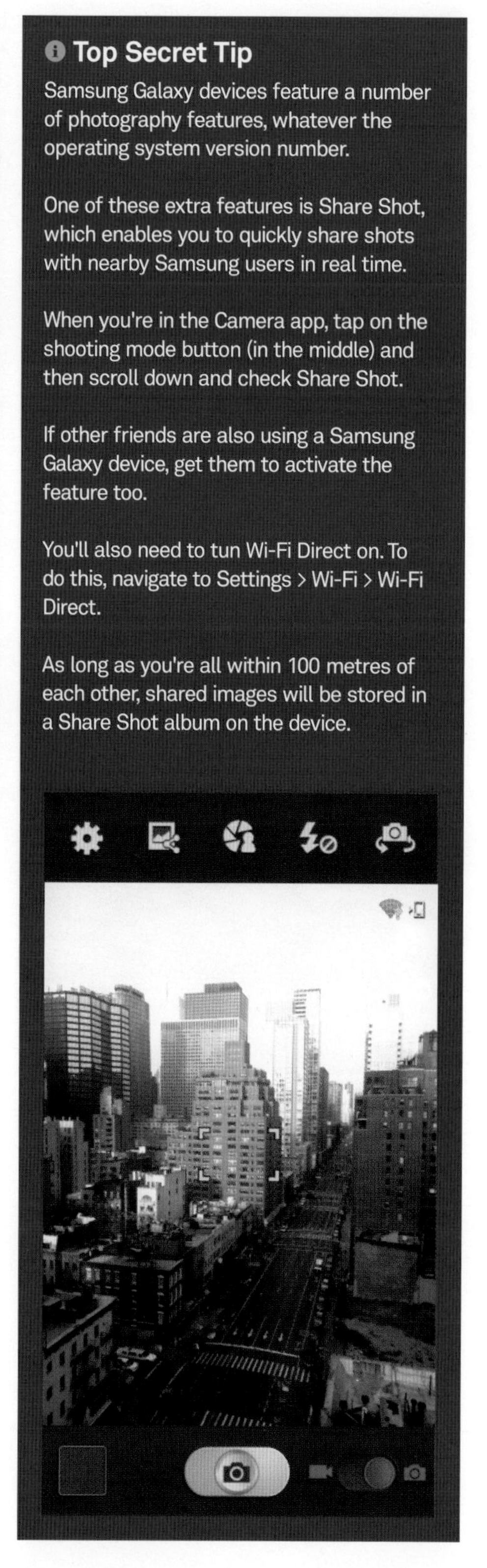

Podcasts

Podcasts have grown and grown in popularity during in recent years. Much of this is to do with the rise and usage of smartphones. Then there's the fact that you can get podcasts about pretty much any subject under the sun – sport, politics, film, sewing, tech, embroidery and more.

With an Android-powered Galaxy device you have some of the best applications for curating and syncing all of your favourite podcasts between your PC and your phone. Here's a selection of some of the best.

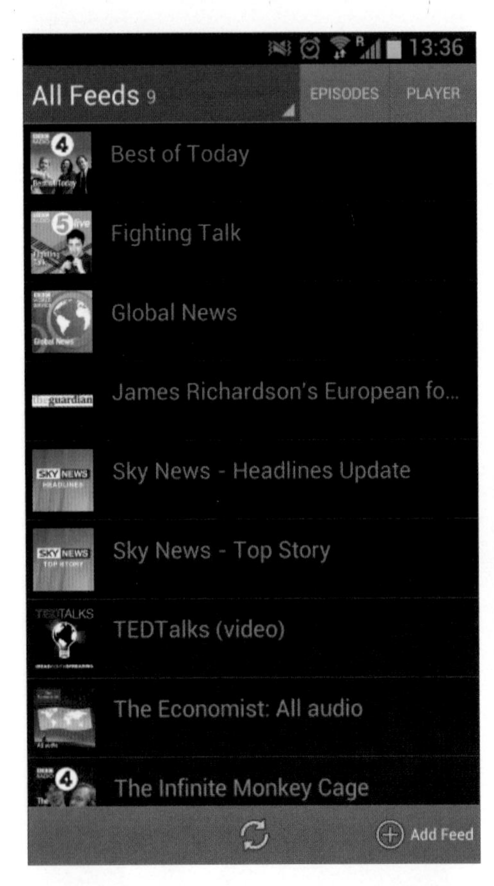

BeyondPod
The daddy of all podcast managers, BeyondPod is easily one of the best applications available on Google's Play store. Check RSS feeds, listen and watch podcasts and keep everything in order with the app's dedicated podcast manager.

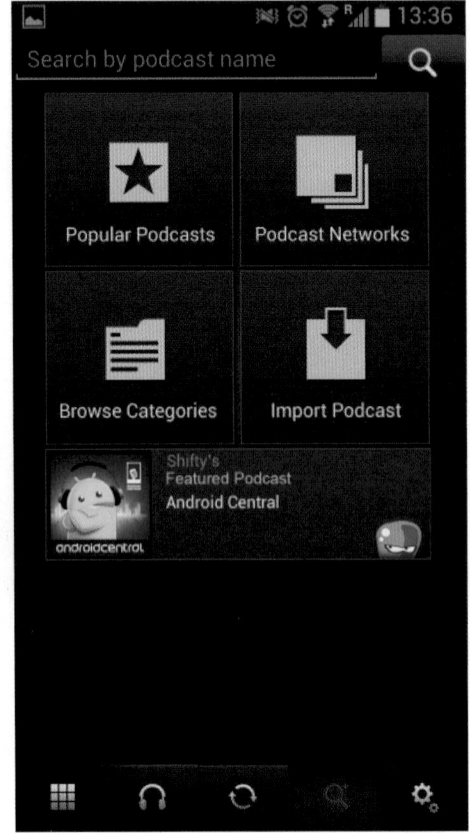

Pocket Casts
It might cost £1.99 but it's worth every penny, allowing you to stream podcasts over both 3G and Wi-Fi, as well as refreshing up to 100 lists at a time. The UI is simple to navigate around, and it's packed with tons of useful features. If you don't mind paying a premium, it doesn't get much better than this for on-device podcast management.

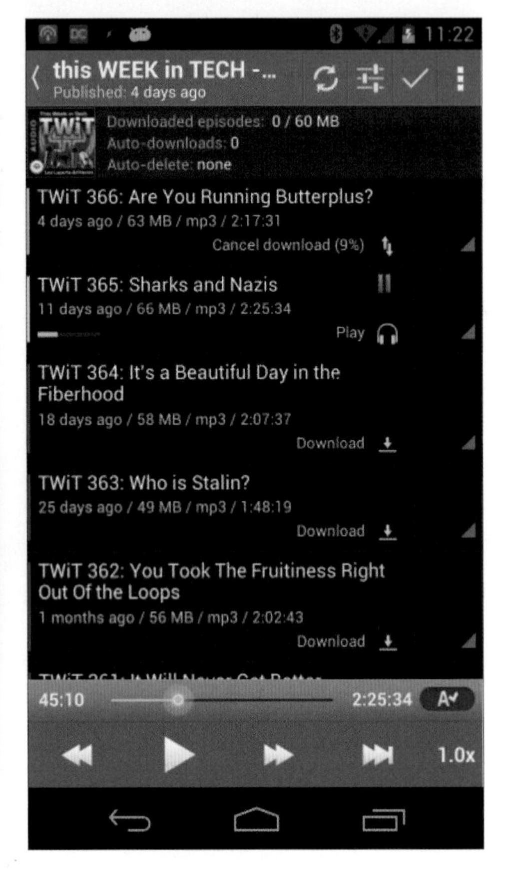

DoggCatcher
DoggCatcher was voted the best podcast manager for Android in 2011, and with good reason too. The app itself is simple to setup and features a myriad of features that make accessing, listening and discovering new podcasts extremely simple. You also get offline playback and there's an 8,000-plus strong community of users active in the DoggCatcher forums.

Google Books

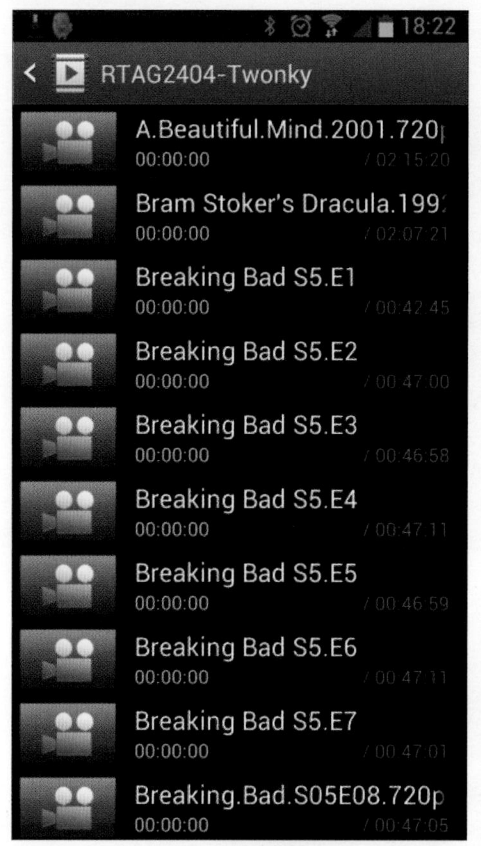

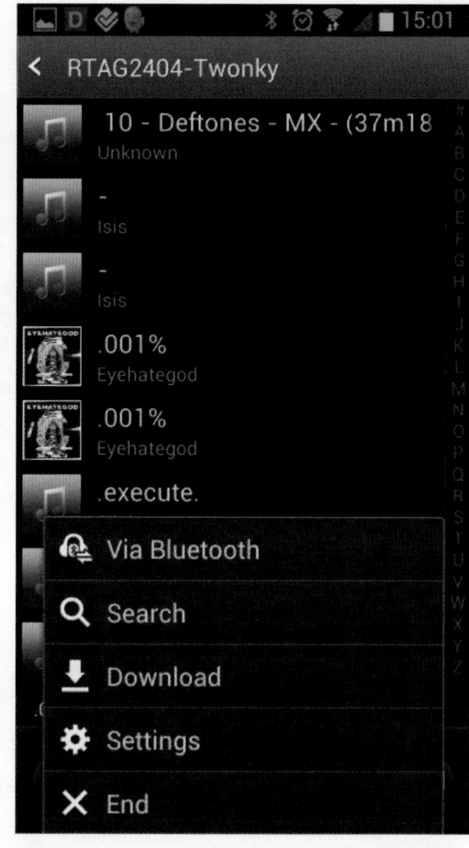

Google's Books service has more than 20 million digital titles, including magazines, newspapers, and comics. Fully integrated into the Play store, browsing content, finding authors, and purchasing new literature has never been easier.

All content inside your Google Books app is synced across all your devices, so if you buy a title on your Galaxy Note 2 it'll also be available on your PC and your Galaxy Tab 10.1 device. It also saves your bookmarks, so you don't even have to worry about losing your place.

Top Secret Tip

You can set your Samsung Galaxy device to display the remaining battery life by percentage to make it clearer how much juice you have left. Go to 'Settings', then 'Display' and then check the 'Display battery percentage' box.

How to download books to your device:

- Open up the Play store
- Tap the 'Books' section
- Inside it's broken up into the following sections: Categories, Featured, Top Selling, New Arrivals in Fiction, New Arrivals in Non-Fiction, and Top Free.
- You can also search for titles by clicking the 'Search' icon
- Once you've found what you're looking for, hit the icon to buy and it'll download to your Play Books application

That's it – it's all very easy: just search, click, and read.

Top Secret Tip

Rooting your Samsung Galaxy device will allow you to install a wider range of applications, books and other content you may want to use on your handset. Be warned though, although rooting can add a whole lot more functionality, if you get it wrong, it can 'brick' your device, making in as useful as, well, a brick.

Although the process of rooting your Android device is pretty much the same whatever you're using, it will vary depending on the model and model number. This guide refers to rooting your Sam

Make sure you have version 1.85 of ODIN, Samsung's smartphone software management tool - it can be downloaded from forum.xda-developers.com/attachment.php?attachmentid=581913&d=1304094576

You should also download the root package for your specific device.

After your download completes, unzip the file and place the resulting .tar file somewhere memorable. We recommend your desktop.

Open ODIN and click the button marked 'PDA'.

Choose the .tar file you unzipped earlier.

Next, we're going to need to put your Galaxy into download mode. We achieve this by switching the device off, waiting 10 seconds and then switching it back on again whilst simultaneously holding down 'Home', 'Volume Down' and the 'Power' key.

Once you've done that, plug your device into your computer, click 'Start' and wait a moment.

Ensure that you do not unplug your device as this may result in damage. Once the procedure is complete your device will be rooted.

Chapter 7

Productivity

Creating and editing Word documents on your Samsung Galaxy

You can use your Samsung Galaxy phone or tablet to get some work done while away from the office. There are a number of third-party Office suite apps that allow you to view and edit Microsoft Office documents. DocsToGo is one of our favourites.

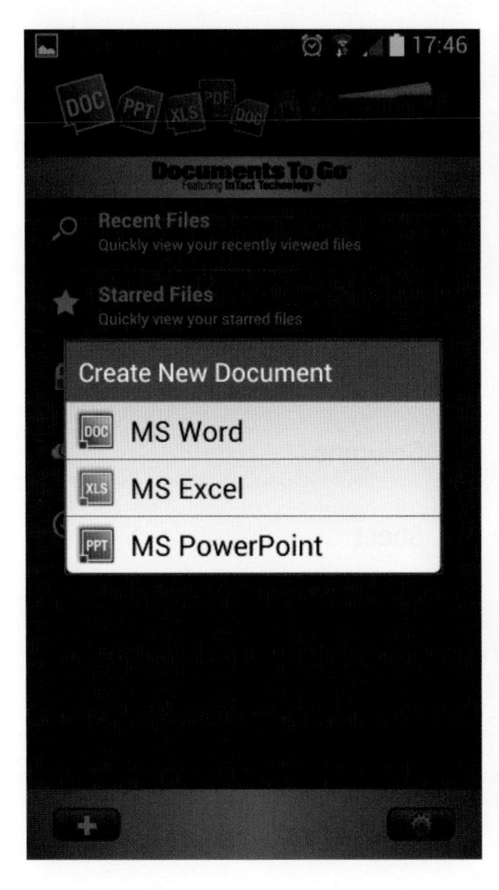

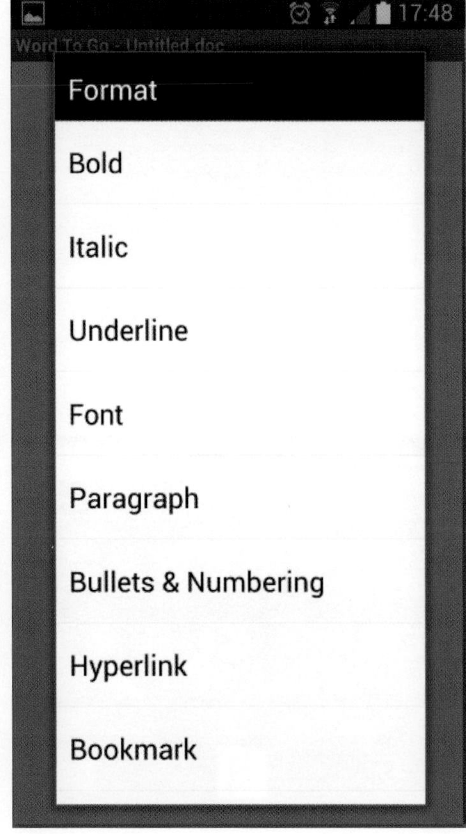

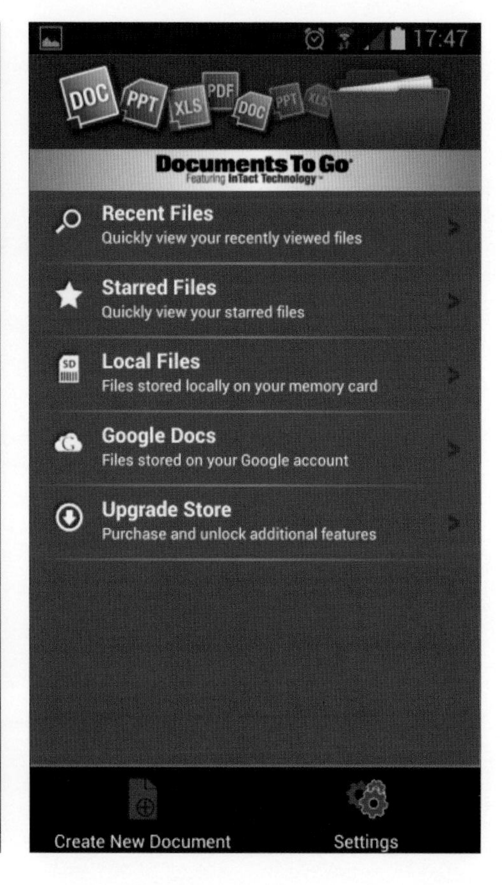

With DocsToGo you can save and access files from your phone's storage or link a Google Drive cloud account.

To create a new document

- Tap the '+' icon. Alternatively, in the main DocsToGo screen press your phone's 'Menu' key and tap 'Create new document.'
- Select MS Word from the pop-up list. You'll now be in a new document with the touch keyboard in the lower part of the screen.

Hint: To access key Word functions tap the phone's 'Menu' key.

'File' - allows you to create new documents, open existing documents, close the current document, save changes, save the document under a new file name or send the document via email.

'Edit' - allows you to toggle the touch keyboard, select sections of text, select all text, cut, copy, paste, undo and redo.

'View' - allows you to adjust zoom, find words in the page or edit footnotes.

'Format' - allows you to format the document with bold, italic or underlining functions, font style, paragraphs and indentation, bullet points and numbering, hyperlinks and bookmarks.

'Insert' - lets you add page breaks, bookmarks, hyperlinks and tables.

'More' -opens up options for 'Preferences', file properties and word count.

Top alternatives

- Kingsoft Office
- Quickoffice Pro
- ThinkFree Office
- OfficeSuite Pro
- Smart Office

Top Secret Tip

You can encrypt your Samsung Galaxy and the SD card for increased security. Go into 'Settings', tap on 'Security' and then tap on either 'Encrypt device' or 'Encrypt SD card'. Once you've tapped these, you'll go through the on-screen instructions for securing your device further.

Creating and editing Excel spreadsheets on your Samsung Galaxy

DocsToGo and similar Office suites can also be used to create and edit Excel spreadsheets while on the move.

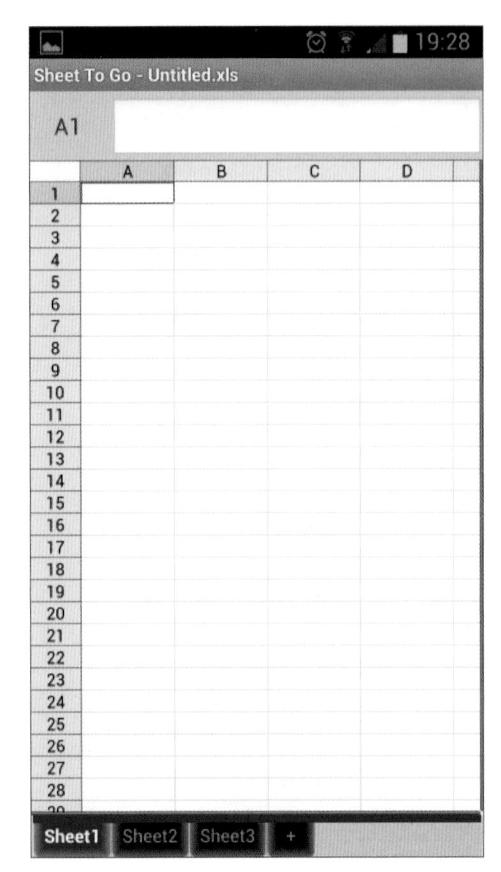

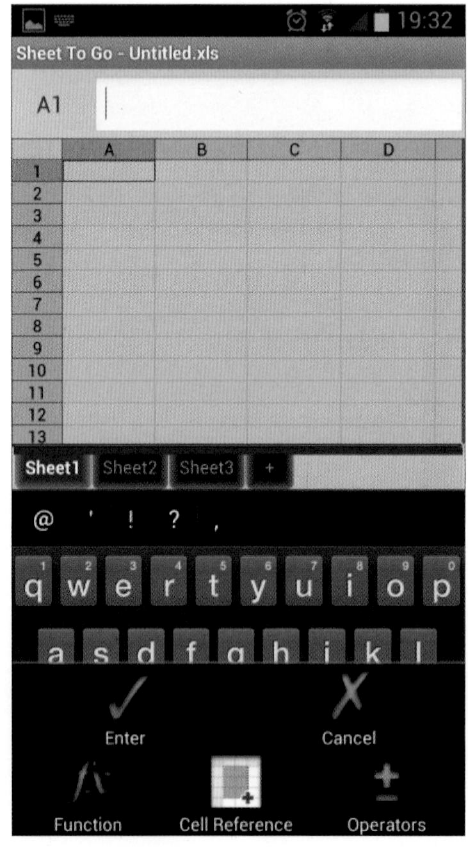

To create a new spreadsheet

- Tap the '+' icon. Alternatively, in the main DocsToGo screen press your phone's 'Menu' key and tap 'Create new document.'
- Select MS Excel from the pop-up list. You'll now be in a new Excel spreadsheet document.

Editing a document

- You can pan around the document with your finger or use pinch-to-zoom for magnification.
- Tapping on a box allows you to edit the contents of the box. With a box selected, tap on the bar at the top of the screen - the touch keyboard will appear.

Tap the phone's 'Menu' key to bring up the contextual controls. From here you can:

- Use 'Function' to edit the cell function.
- Tap 'Cell reference' to insert the cell reference ID.
- Use 'Operators' to add operators to the cell.
- Remember to use the 'Enter' control to complete your formulae, or if you want to start again you can tap 'Cancel' instead.
- At the bottom of the page there are tabs for three sheets by default. You can tap the '+' icon to add more.

Without the cell function bar selected you can tap the phone's 'Menu' key to bring up a different set of contextual controls:

'File' - allows you to create new documents, open existing documents, close the current document, save the current document, save the document with a new file name or send the document via email.
'Edit' - allows you to edit a currently selected cell, to select text or formulae in the document body and provides options for cut, copy, paste, undo and redo.
'View' - allows you to control zoom, find keywords in the document, jump between worksheets and view a cell's contents.
'Format' - lets you format numbers, cell settings, sheet settings and provides sorting controls.
'Insert' - lets you input a function, add rows and columns, add sheets, add comments to cells and run the AutoSum formula tool.
'More' - includes options for deleting rows, columns, sheets and comments, with row and column controls.

Creating and editing PowerPoint presentations on your Samsung Galaxy

As well as Word documents and Excel spreadsheets, you can also use your Samsung Galaxy device with apps such as DocsToGo to create and edit PowerPoint presentations.

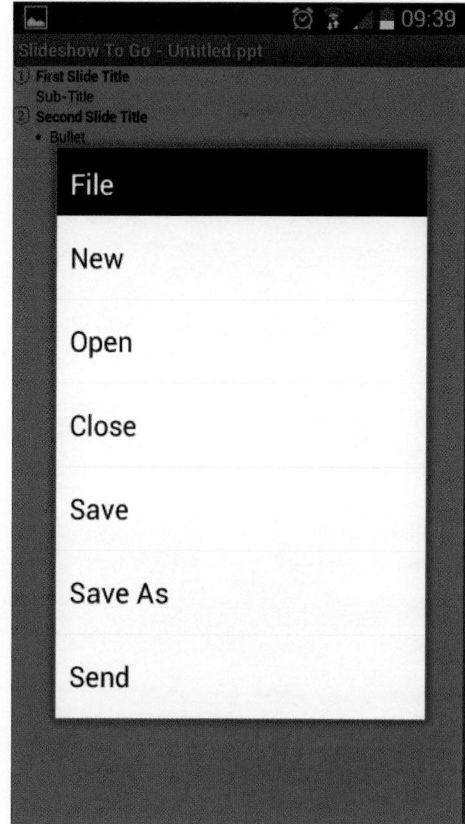

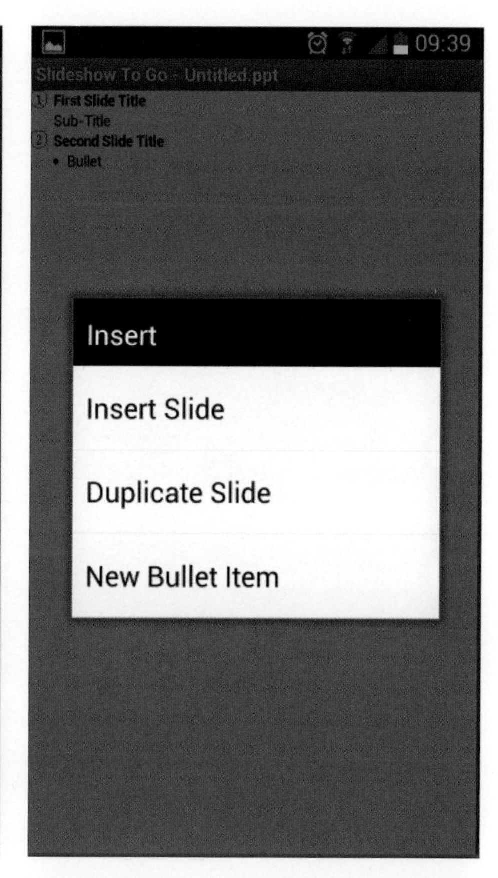

To create a new presentation

- Tap the '+' icon. Alternatively, in the main DocsToGo screen press your phone's 'Menu' key and tap 'Create new document.'
- Select MS PowerPoint from the pop-up list. You'll now be in a new document.
- The touch keyboard should appear, allowing you to edit the text in the presentation's slides. You can zoom in and out by pinching the touchscreen.

Editing controls are accessed by pressing the phone's 'Menu' key.

'File' - allows you to create new documents, open existing documents, close the current document, save the current document, save the document with a new file name or send the document via email.

'Edit' - allows you to toggle the touch keyboard on or off, select content from the document body, perform cut, copy, paste, undo and redo functions, sort slides and delete slides.

'View' - lets you control the zoom, find text in the document, view individual slides, view an overall 'outline' of the presentation (ie: all the slides at once), view notes, move forward and backwards between slides and a quick jump selector for individual slides.

'Format' - allows you to increase or decrease the indent.

'Insert' - lets you add a new slide, duplicate a current slide or add a new bullet item to a slide.

'More' - includes further options for preferences.

Top Secret Tip

You can install apps on your Galaxy directly from your computer. This is an ideal option if you want to install an app on multiple Samsung Galaxy devices, such as tablets and smartphones. Go to play.google.com and, when you're signed into your Google account, choose the app you want to download. Click 'Install' and there will be an option that says 'Send To Another Device...'

Tap on the 'Choose another device on which to install', scroll down to the Samsung Galaxy option and the app will be automatically installed a few seconds later.

A guide to file sharing

Samsung Galaxy devices are made for sharing. A combination of the hardware features and features of Android allow you to send files, pictures or videos to friends wherever they are in the world.

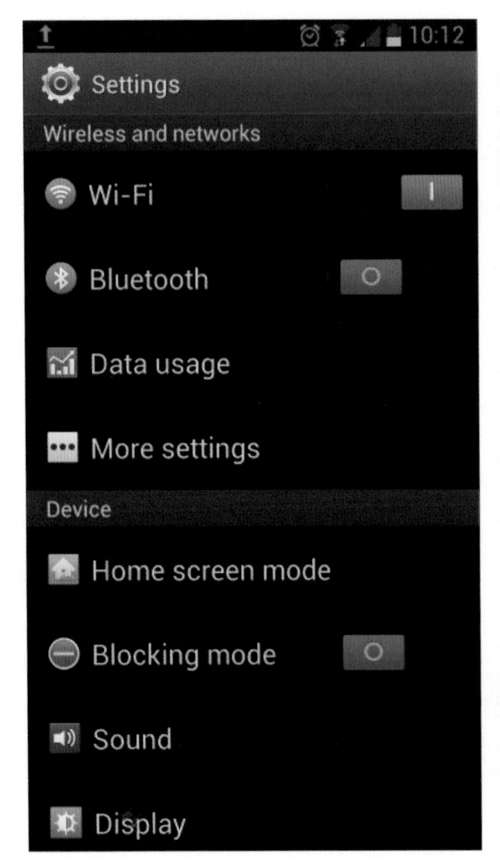

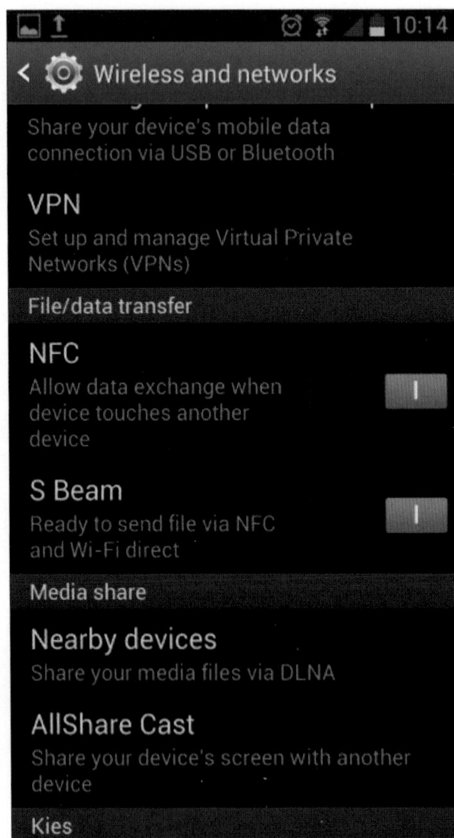

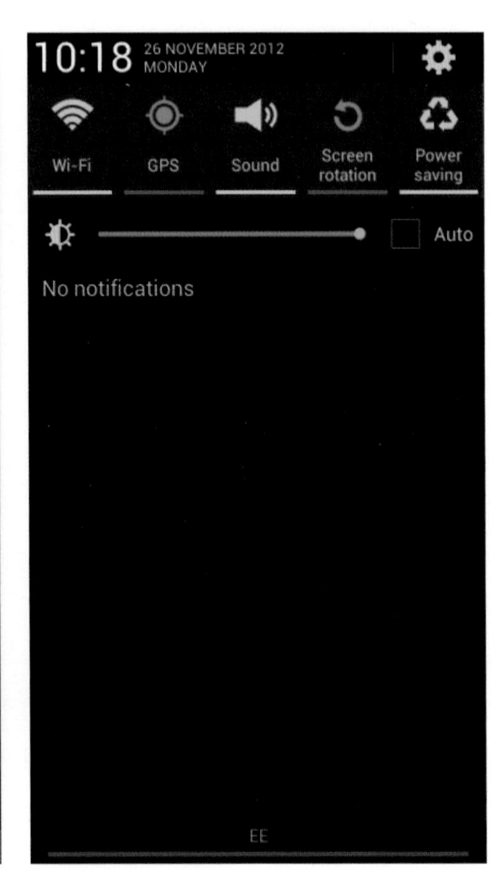

NFC
Not all Samsung Galaxy phones are NFC enabled, but with the most recently released and premium models it's becoming a more commonly included capability. On Samsung Galaxy models with TouchWiz you have to use the 'S Beam' functionality for NFC (on the Galaxy Nexus there's Android Beam instead).

How to share files with NFC:

- Open 'Settings.'
- On TouchWiz models (such as the Galaxy S III) tap 'More settings' followed by 'S Beam.' On Galaxy Nexus models tap 'Wireless and networks,' then tap 'More,' followed by 'Android Beam.'
- Ensure NFC is switched on with the toggle control.
- Ensure that S Beam or Android Beam is switched on with the toggle control.
- Find and open the item you want to share, such as a photo, document or video.
- Hold the device back-to-back with another NFC-enabled device. You may hear a sound and be greeted with a prompt. Tap any on-screen prompts to complete the process, it should only take a few moments to send the data between devices.

Bluetooth
Bluetooth can also be used to share data/files in a similar fashion to NFC, though to do so doesn't require you to 'bump' devices together. Bluetooth is also a far more commonly included capability on most smartphones and tablets.

How to share files with Bluetooth:

- To activate Bluetooth go into 'Settings.'
- In 'Wireless and networks' you should find a Bluetooth toggle. Ensure this is switched on. Note that on many Samsung Galaxy handsets you can also find a Bluetooth toggle directly from the homescreen - it's in the quick settings menu on the drop-down notifications bar.
- Pair your phone with another Bluetooth device you wish to share data with by scanning for and selecting the device. You may need to enter a key.
- With Bluetooth activated and the phone paired, navigate to the file you wish to share and open it.
- Tap the share symbol (it looks like a series of dots connected by lines)
- Find and tap the Bluetooth icon (you may have to tap 'see all' and scroll through the icons).
- The phone should now scan for available devices. Select the device you want to share with. The data transfer should only take a few moments.

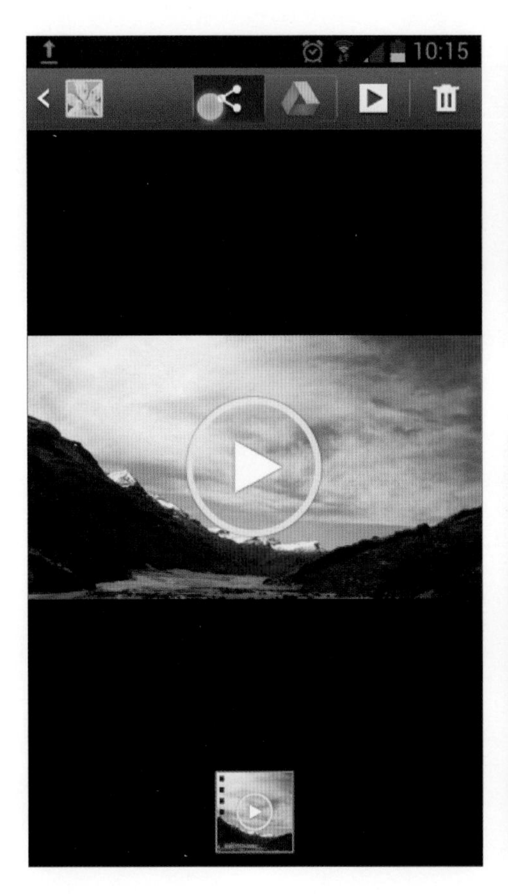

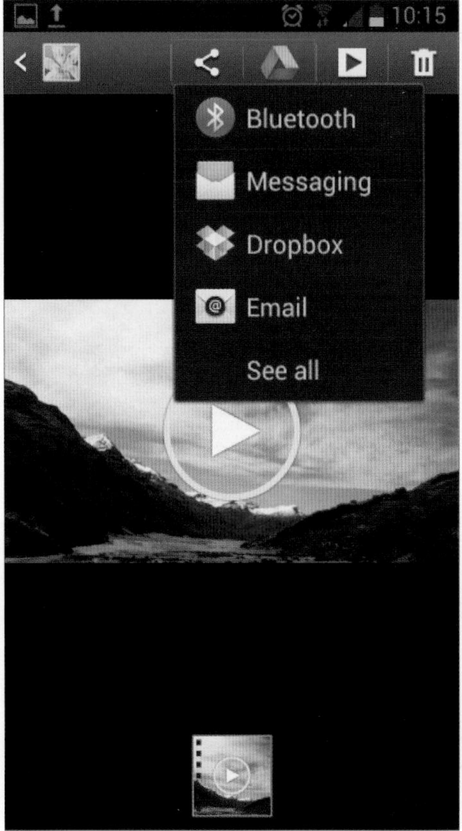

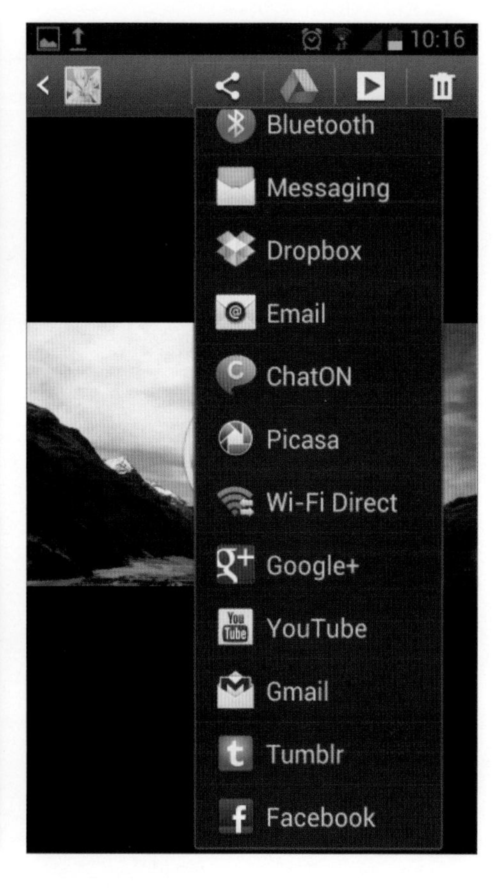

Email

To share content via email you need to have an email account setup on your Samsung Galaxy device already. This can be a Gmail account, a webmail account such as Hotmai]
l or Yahoo, or a Microsoft Exchange email account.

How to share via email:

- To share an item such as a photo or video, open the file you wish to send.
- Tap the share icon.
- Tap 'See all' to show a full list of sharing options.
- Select the email account you wish to share through from the list.
- You'll be taken to a new email with the file attached, simply add one or more recipients, a subject line and some body text.
- Tap 'Send'.

Messaging and social networking

You can share files and content through a number of messaging channels, including MMS text messages from your phone number, Facebook Chat, ChatOn or through social networking apps such as Facebook, Twitter and Google +.

In each case it works in exactly same way as the email method described here. Simply open the item you wish to share and tap the share icon, followed by the method you want to use to share - you'll need to enter recipients and other message details but your item should be already attached.

Cloud

Cloud services are another handy way of sharing data. We cover Google Drive in more detail later in this book, where we explain how you can share individual documents with other users.

You can also directly share via Google Drive from any file you like by tapping the share icon and selecting 'Drive' from the list. You can then choose to add it to a shared folder.

You can do the same with Dropbox, another useful cloud storage and sharing service, if you install the dedicated app on your Samsung Galaxy device and set up an account.

Web browsing with Samsung Galaxy

Android's built-in WebKit browser is a decent offering with pinch-zoom, double-tap controls and tab functionality. It's also quick, syncs with your Google account, features offline browsing and supports a number of Chrome features such as Incognito mode.

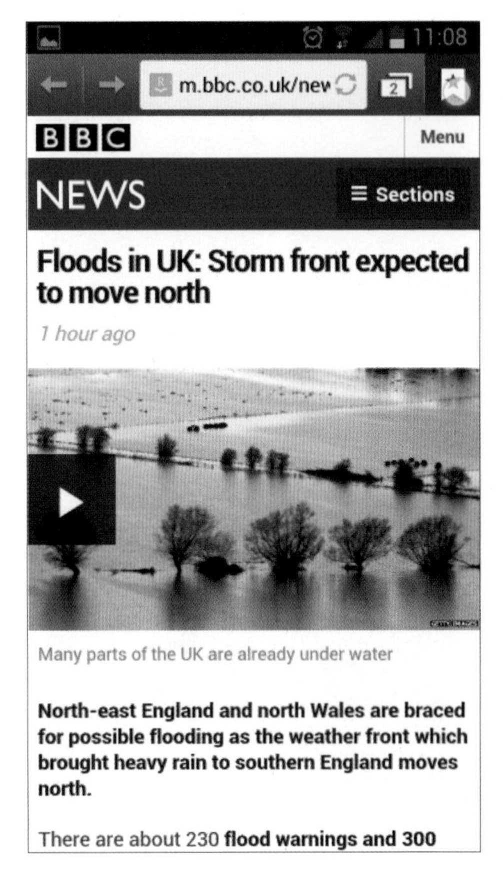

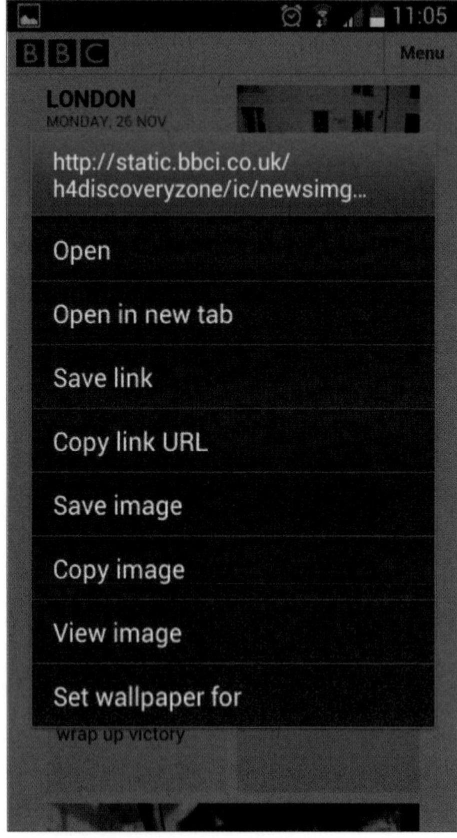

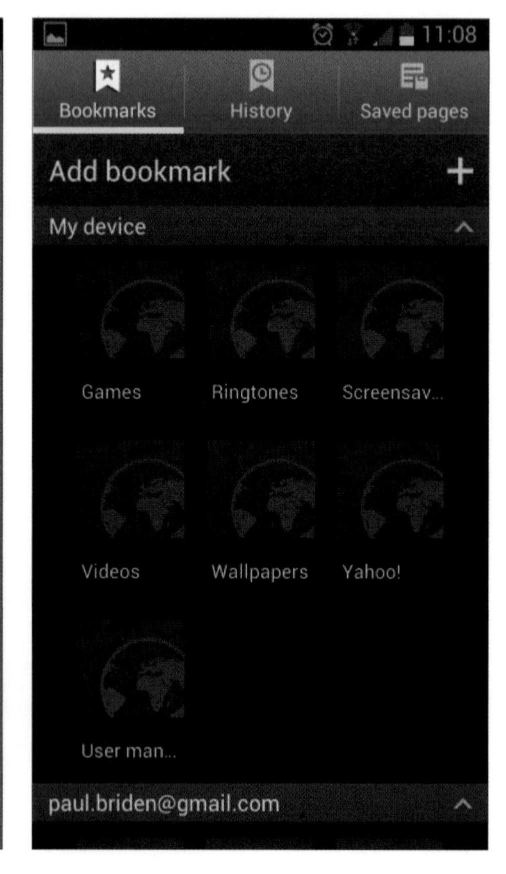

How to view a web page:

- Open the browser by tapping on the 'Internet' shortcut.
- Tap on the address bar. Here you can either type a direct URL (such as www.bbc.co.uk) or type in a search term using Google Search. Suggested searches will come up as you type and you can tap one to go straight into the search.
- If you chose to search you can now scroll through Google's results and tap on any you want to visit.

Hint: Press and hold on a link at any time to bring up an actions menu - you can select 'Open in new tab' to bring up the page while keeping the page you're currently on in the background'

Other controls:
While viewing a page, tap your phone's 'Menu' key. From here, you can perform a number of actions: 'New window' opens a new tab while keeping your current page in the background.

Hint: you can also press the 'Tabs' button to the immediate right of the address bar. Here you can view a carousel of all open pages, tapping on one will open it as your main page, you can close pages with the '-' icon, open new pages with the '+' icon or open an incognito (private) page with the 'Spy' icon.
'Share page' lets you share the web page via messaging or social networking.
'Bookmark this page' lets you add the page to your favourites.
'Save for offline reading' lets you save the page to view when you don't have an internet connection.

Hint: the star icon in the top right allows you to access your bookmarks, browsing history and saved pages. It also lets you access favourites saved on your Google account via Google Chrome on computers or mobile devices.

Top alternative browsers:

- Google Chrome
- Opera Mini/Opera Mobile
- Dolphin
- Firefox
- Skyfire

Using Google Search on your Samsung Galaxy

Google's built-in search function not only allows you to search the web, it can also be used to search your phone for contacts, favourite web pages, content and apps.

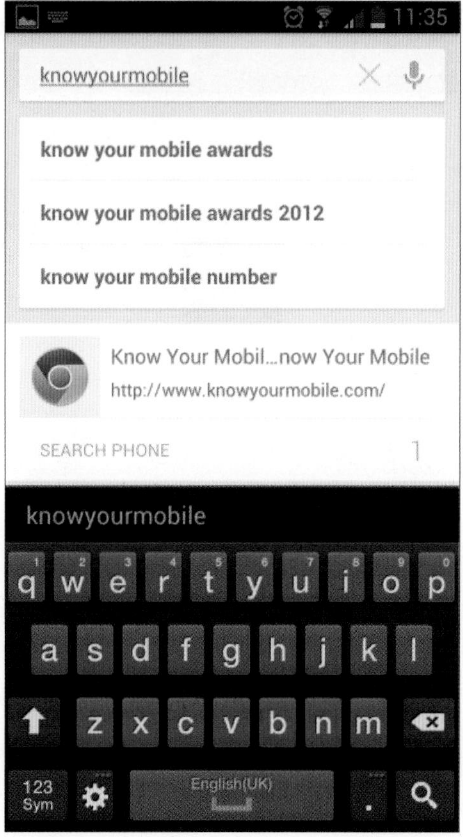

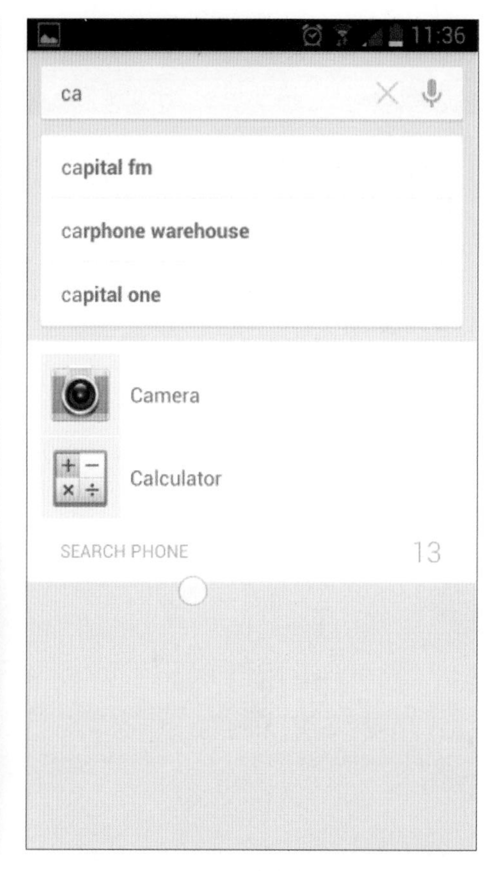

To use Google search, simply tap on the search bar and begin typing.

If you haven't got the Google search bar widget on your homescreen, go into your App Drawer and tap the 'Google' shortcut instead.

- As you type a search term suggestions will pop up. If you're connected to the internet you'll see web search suggestions.
- You can tap a suggested search term or ignore them and type your own terms completely.
- Tap the magnifying glass on the keyboard to complete the search - this will perform a dedicated web search.

Whether you have an internet connection or not you'll also see 'Search phone' suggestions coming up with apps, contacts and browser favourites.

At any point you can tap 'Search phone' to do a dedicated phone search using the search terms and this will show you all possible results.

With any search there should be a scrollable bar at the bottom of the page. You're able to select from 'Web', 'Images' or 'Places', or you can tap 'Phone' to look at possible apps, contacts, eBooks and so on. You can also tap 'More', to expand the scrollable bar with other Google search options such as 'Shopping', 'News' and 'Video'.

Tapping the cross on a search term will remove it from the suggestions list. If you tap the cross in the search bar it will remove your current search completely, allowing you to start again.

Top Secret Tip

While your Samsung Galaxy has a solid on-screen keyboard, you may just want to use a physical one.

The easiest solution is to get a Bluetooth keyboard and then go into the tablet or smartphone's settings, turn on Bluetooth, hit the 'Search for devices' button and it should recognise your keyboard (make sure it's turned on).

From there, you'll get on-screen pairing instructions and you should be able to use your keyboard anywhere on the Galaxy where there's text input.

Using Google Drive on your Samsung Galaxy

Google Drive (formerly Google Docs) is Google's synchronised cloud service which spans web, computer and mobile content.

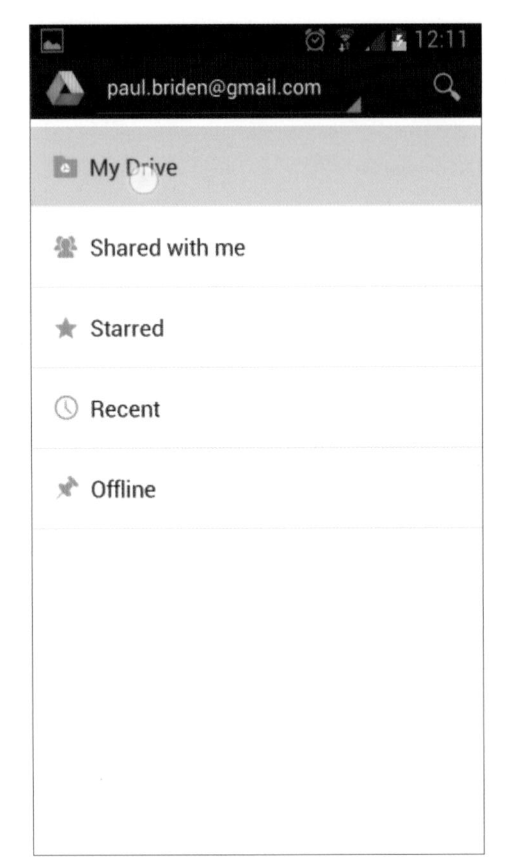

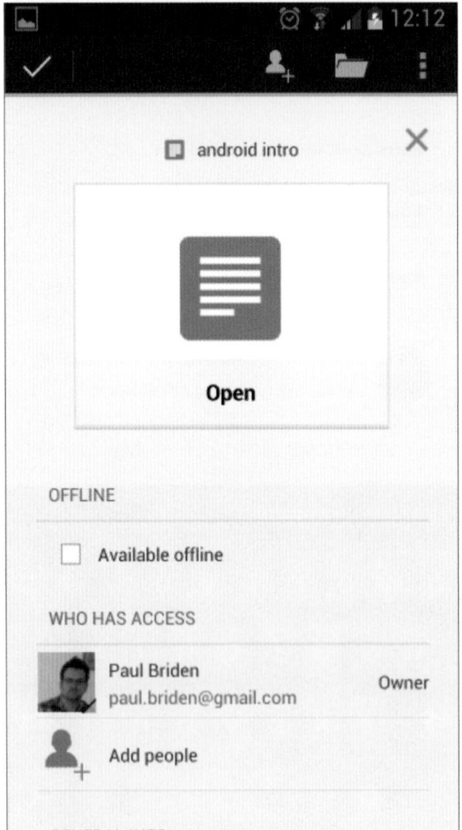

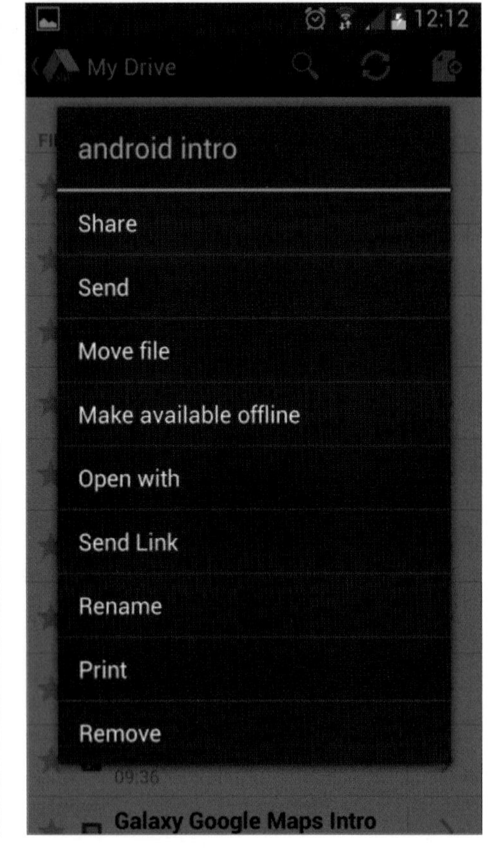

Google Drive is an excellent way of making key documents available to you at all times, wherever you are. You can download the Google Drive app from Google Play and it will automatically sync with an active Google account on your phone.

When you open Google Drive you'll be presented with the main page. Here you'll find categories for 'My Drive', 'Shared with me', 'Starred' (favourites), 'Recent' and 'Offline'.

If you have multiple Google accounts you can switch between them by tapping the bar at the top and selecting from the drop-down list. There's also a search function in the top right to help you quickly find documents.

'My Drive' is the main component of Google Drive as this is where you'll see every document you've created on your phone, tablet or computer. You can scroll through your files, tap them to view or check the star icon to make them favourites.

- Tapping the arrow icon to the right shows you a document preview. Here you can edit who has access to the file and make it available offline if you wish. A drop-down menu in the top right also allows you to send it via email, rename the document, print it or delete it.

Hint: in the file browser in the 'My Drive' section you can also perform a number of actions simply by pressing and holding on the file and selecting from the pop-up menu.

- You can create new documents by tapping on the paper icon with a '+' in the top right corner. You can choose from new folders, spreadsheets or text documents, or to take a photo with the phone to be saved in Google Drive.

- When viewing a document, you can simply scroll around and pinch-to-zoom to navigate. You can edit the document by double tapping within the body or by pressing the pencil icon in the top bar. This will bring up a scrollable formatting bar at the top and the touch keyboard in the lower part of the display. After making any changes, hit the tick icon to complete.

- You can also tap the speech bubble to leave a comment for shared users, or add users to the shared list with the icon in the top right corner.

Using Google Cloud Print on your Samsung Galaxy

Google Cloud Print allows you to print documents wherever you are from your mobile device (as long as you have a data or Wi-Fi connection). You need a Google account and the Google Drive app installed on your Samsung Galaxy device.

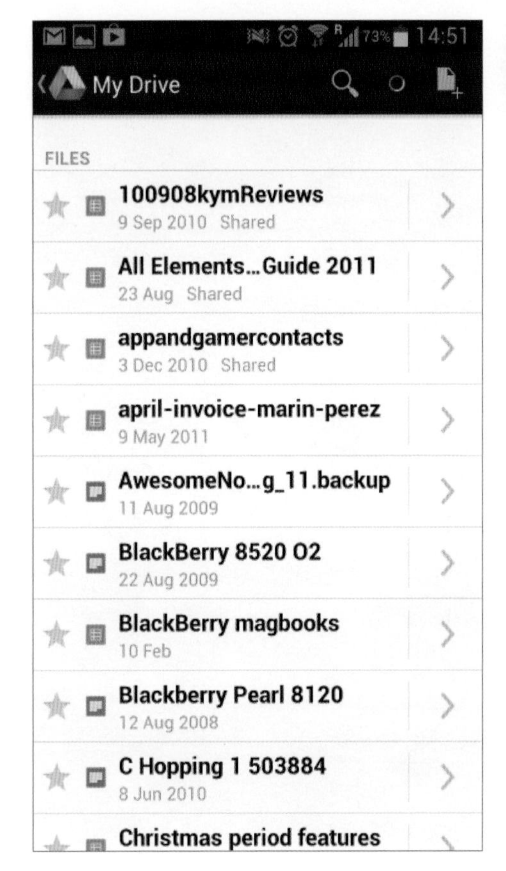

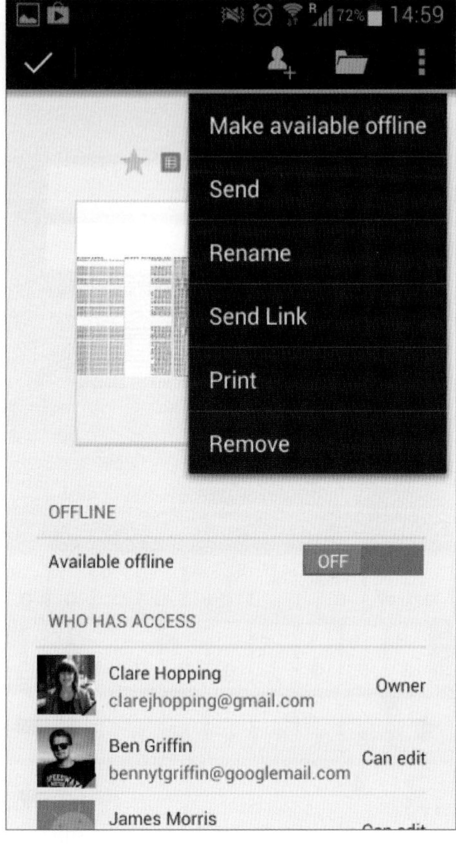

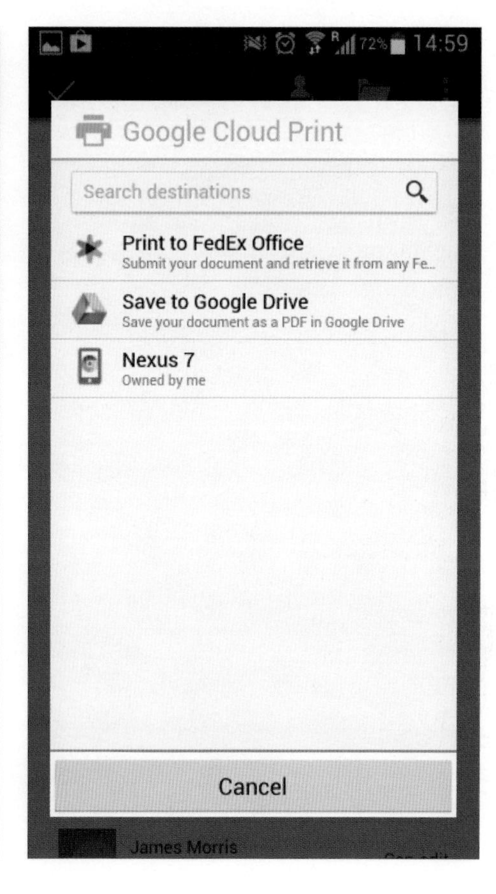

There are a number of cloud-ready printers available and you can find a list of compatible models at http://www.google.com/cloudprint/learn/printers.html# where you'll find instructions for setting up each model.

The service also works with regular printers. You'll need a printer already set up and connected to a Mac or a PC with Windows Service Pack 3 and whichever machine you use will need Google Chrome installed.

- Log in to Google Drive on your Samsung Galaxy device by opening the app and entering your Google account details.
- Log in to your Google account in the Chrome browser on your computer by going to the 'Menu' tab.
- In the menu tab, go into the 'Settings' section.
- Click 'Show advanced settings.'
- Click 'Add printer.'
- Confirm by clicking 'Add printer(s).'
- All printers associated with your computer will now be added. You can click 'Manage printers' to inspect, remove and adjust the settings of printers.

How to print from your mobile device:
Once you've taken care of the setup and have your mobile device linked in via the Google Drive app you'll be able to print Google Drive documents from your phone or tablet.

- Open Google Drive.
- Tap 'My Drive.'
- Press and hold on a document you wish to print.
- Tap 'Print' from the options which come up.
- Select a printer from the list of devices that appears.
- You'll be presented with printing options, such as the number of copies to print, colour settings and orientation. When you've configured things to your liking tap 'Print.' After a few moments the document should begin printing.

How to remotely access your computer from a Samsung Galaxy

LogMeIn Ignition allows you to access your computer from your Samsung Galaxy mobile phone or tablet - useful if you're out of the office and need something vital stored on a PC or Mac.

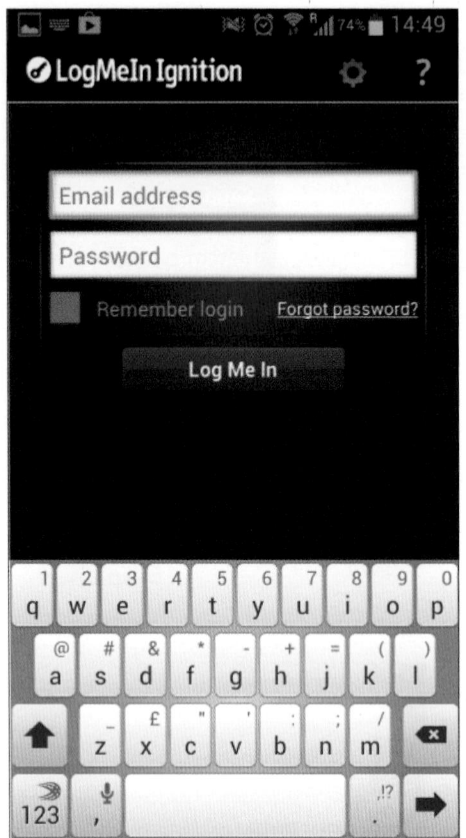

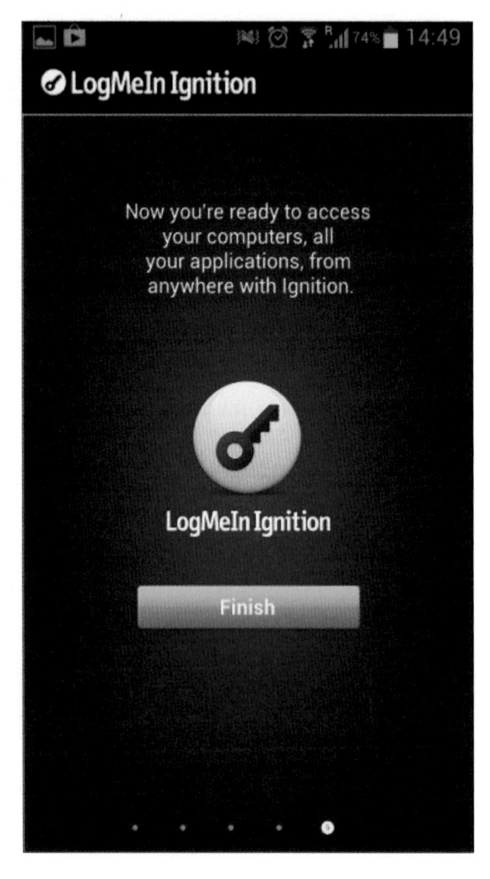

In order to use LogMeIn Ignition you should already have a LogMeIn account. If not, you can create one by visiting the LogMeIn website.

You'll also need to install LogMeIn host software (LogMeIn Pro² or LogMeIn Free) onto your computer and to have logged in from that machine - this will have added the computer to your LogMeIn profile.

To install LogMeIn Pro² or LogMeIn Free, go to the computer that you want to be able to access remotely and log in to your account at www.LogMeIn.com.

- Click 'Add Computer' on the My Computers page.
- Follow all on-screen instructions.

Once you've done this and have installed the app on your phone or tablet from the Google Play store, you can get started with remote access.

Using LogMeIn on your mobile device:

- Open the LogMeIn Ignition app and you'll be prompted with a login page.
- Enter the username and password of your LogMeIn account. You can check the 'Remember login' box if you wish.
- Tap 'Log Me In.'
- You will now be presented with a list of computers you've added. You can connect to any that are listed as 'online.'

In order to be classed as online a computer must meet the following criteria:

- The host computer must be turned on.
- The host computer must not be in sleep mode or hibernation mode.
- The host computer must be connected to the internet.
- The LogMeIn service must be running on the host computer.

Hint: You can create and use multiple LogMeIn profiles. To use a different profile on your phone tap the phone's 'Menu' key. Tap 'Profile' and select the one you want to use.

- To access an online computer simply tap on its entry in the list.

- You may be prompted to enter access details depending on how you setup the computer when you added it to your profile. This may require either the computer's existing login username and password (ie: what you'd use to login if you were sitting at the computer) or a specific access code. One again, you may check the 'Remember' box to save the login details if you wish.

- Tap 'Log In' to complete the process.

How to use data management on your Samsung Galaxy

Samsung Galaxy devices have built-in data management so you can control just how much mobile internet data you consume over your 3G/4G tariff.

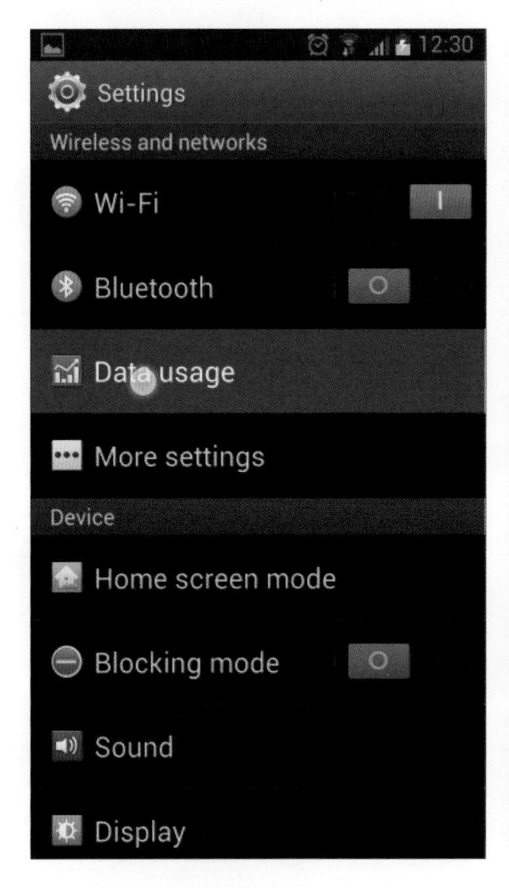

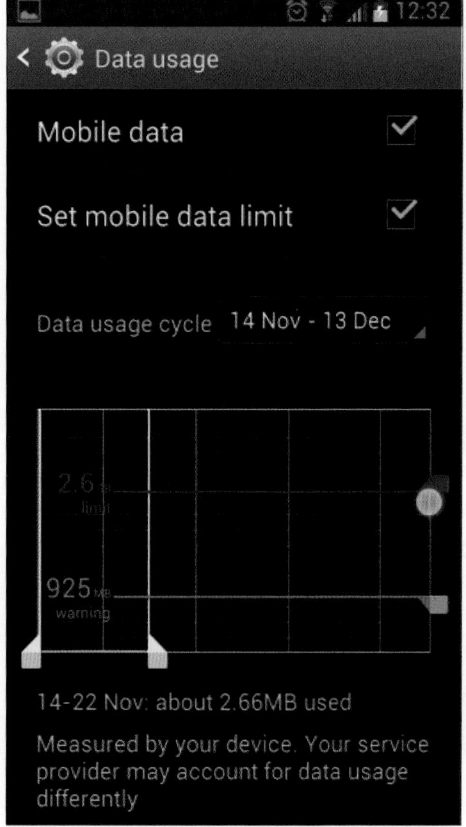

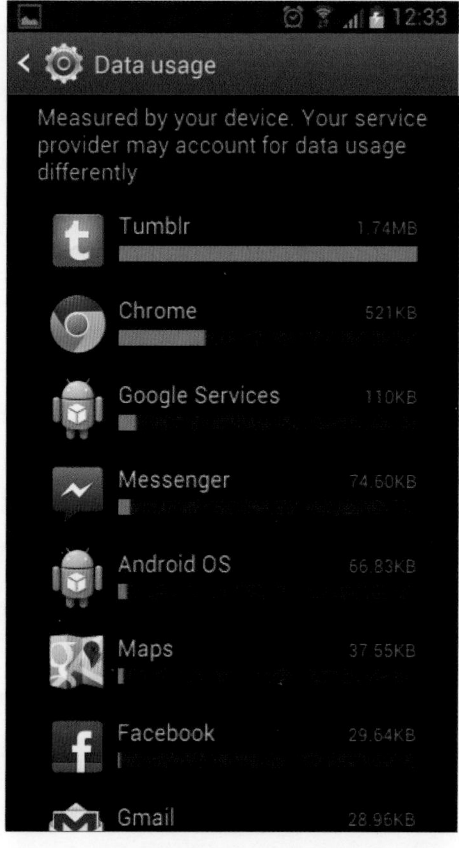

Assuming you're not on an unlimited data plan, it can be useful to set a data limit in order to ensure you don't go over your tariff allowance and incur additional charges from your network.

How to set a data limit:

- Open the 'Settings' menu.
- Tap 'Data usage.'
- If it's not already enabled, tap the 'Mobile data' checkbox to switch on your data connection.
- Check the 'Set mobile data limit' box.
- If a pop-up appears, tap 'OK.'
- You can now drag the red bar to seta data limit in megabytes (MB) or gigabytes (GB).

You can also set the orange bar to give you a warning when you reach a certain point of usage. When your usage meets the red bar limit your data connection will automatically switch off.

Hint: Below the graph there's a selection of apps sorted in order of which you use the most (data wise) and showing how much data you have used in a given time period.

- You can tap on individual apps to get a more detailed view. Some apps may be primarily based around syncing background data, such as email or social networking apps, and these can make data control tricky.

- Within each app's detailed report you can individually toggle the 'Restrict background data' box to ensure these apps only use data when you actively use them.

Top Secret Tip

You can add a number of shortcuts to your Samsung Galaxy device using the accessibility menu.

You can opt to hang up or end a call just by tapping the power button. To do this, head to Settings > Accessibility > Call answering/ending and choose 'The power key ends calls' option.

From this menu, you can also choose to have the home button set up to answer calls more efficiently. Just select 'Answering key' from the same menu.

Chapter 8

Samsung S Features

S Features overview

Despite there being a lot of great phones out there, the Samsung Galaxy S III was, in many eyes, the best of 2012. Why? In addition to the power, pixels and poise it packed in spades, the S III introduced Samsung's S Features. These fantastic, quirky and innovative enhancements added value and, most importantly, differentiation to what could very easily have been just another great bit of kit.

What's more, Samsung didn't settle for two or three features, it introduced an entire library.

Top Secret Tip

You can easily make your Samsung Galaxy's screen orientation lock however you're holding it. Simply pull down the notification bar and tap the screen rotation icon in the menu.

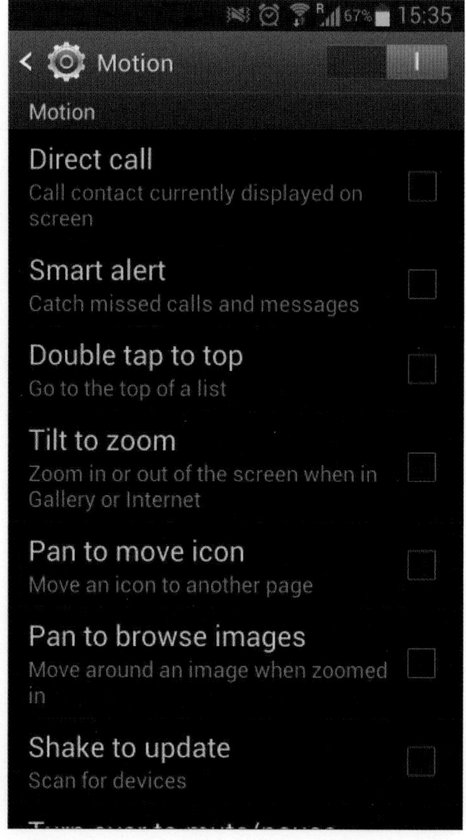

Motion

- We're going to begin by mentioning the 'Motion' menu in the settings. While not S Applications, they're very cool Galaxy exclusive features. Direct Dial ,for example, rings a contact automatically when you put the phone to your ear. Another is tap to top, scrolling to the top of any list you're viewing with little more than a double tap of the top of your Samsung Galaxy phone.

- There are many more of these, so hop over into your settings to see if they're available on your Galaxy. They'll all be under 'Motion' options where you'll find explanations and even diagrams if your phone supports them.

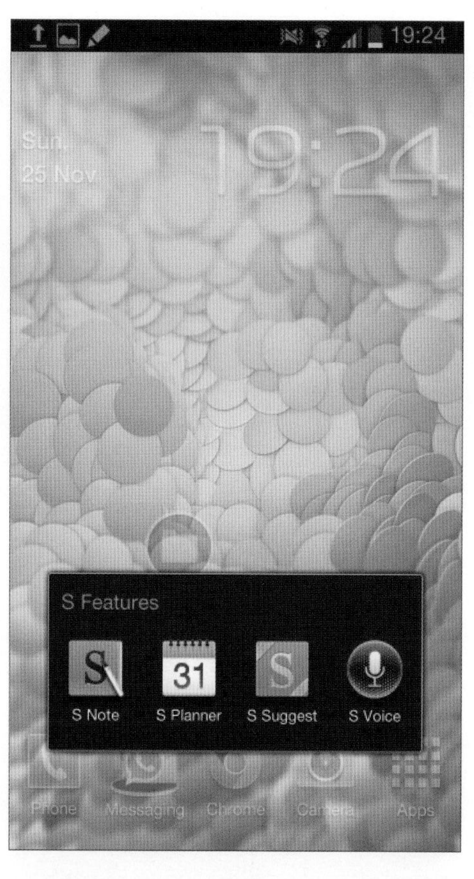

S Features

- What we will explore in depth though is Smart Stay, the tech that keeps the screen on when you're looking at your phone. We'll also look at S Note, S Planner, S Voice and S Suggest - all part of Samsung's app suite.

- For all you Galaxy owners out there who don't have Samsung's application suite, fear not. We share our top social apps with you as well. Starting with Twitter and Facebook, we then move onto Google Talk and Skype, as well as other recommendations.

So what are you waiting for? Turn the page! Your S Features journey has just begun.

Smart Stay

You'll likely be aware of Smart Stay from the Samsung Galaxy S III adverts that aired when the phone was first launched back in May 2012. In short, this neat bit of tech wizardry keeps the phone's screen on while you're looking at it. Then, when you stop looking, it lets the screen sleep.

Top Secret Tip

Larger text can be nice on weary eyes, so it's pretty simple to expand the text on your Samsung Galaxy, whether you're using a tablet, phablet or smartphone.

Go to Settings, click Accessibility and then select the size of text you require.

By deafault, the text size will be set to normal.

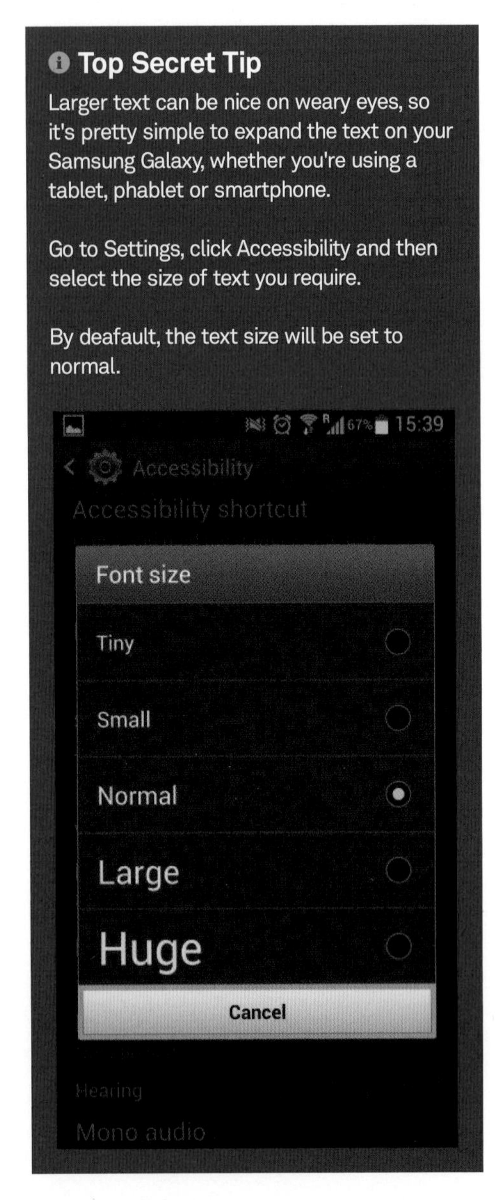

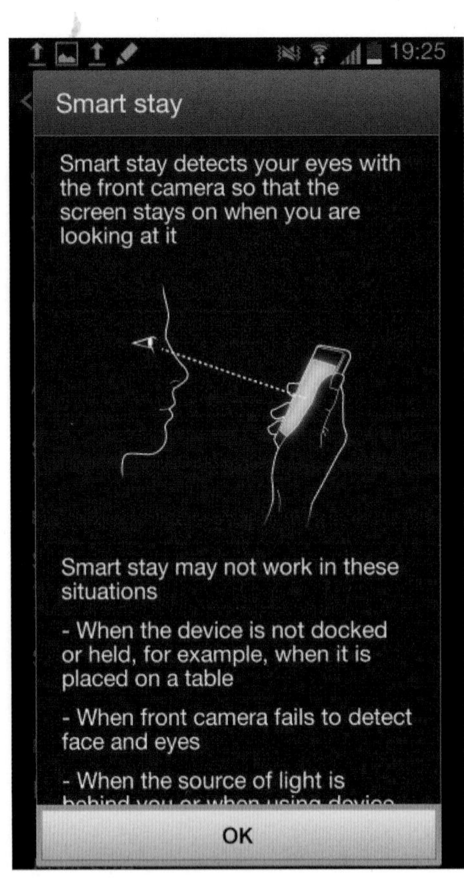

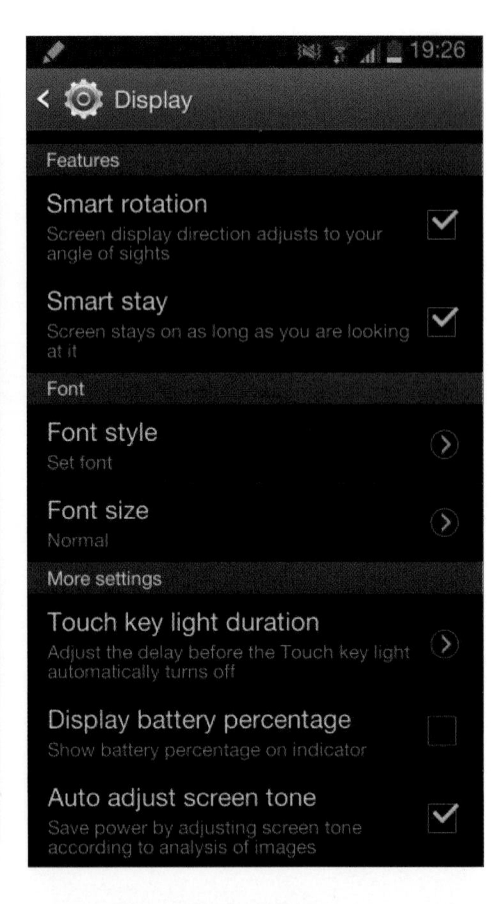

How does it work?

- While we may call it wizardry for convenience, the science behind it is actually pretty simple to explain. Your Samsung Galaxy device's front-facing camera simply takes a peek at your face every time it's about to dim the screen and send your phone to sleep. Mapping your face and, more specifically, your eyes, the phone manages to work out whether your eyes are open and you're staring at your phone or tablet.

- Available on most mid to high end Galaxy devices released post-S III, Smart Stay can be hit or miss, but if it works with your eyes, it's definitely worth using - saving you time tapping the screen to stop it sleeping and unlocking your phone unnecessarily.

How do I turn it on and off?

- Despite being easy to activate, Smart Stay isn't immediately obvious to locate in the settings menu. Rather than being thrown into the 'Motion' options we mentioned earlier, as it has nothing to do with motion Samsung has opted to put it in your 'Display' options.

- To access it, pull down your notifications bar and tap the cog in the top right. This takes you into 'Settings'. Scroll down until you find your 'Display' options under the 'Device' section. Tap it and you'll see within the 'Smart Features' section, the 'Smart Stay' option. Check the box next door and you'll activate it, turning your Galaxy handset's front facing camera into a watchful eye that knows exactly when you're looking.

S Note

If you've got a Samsung Galaxy Note, Note 2 or Note 10.1, lucky, lucky you. Not only do you have a very powerful device on your hands, you've also got an S-Pen, the next evolution of Stylus.

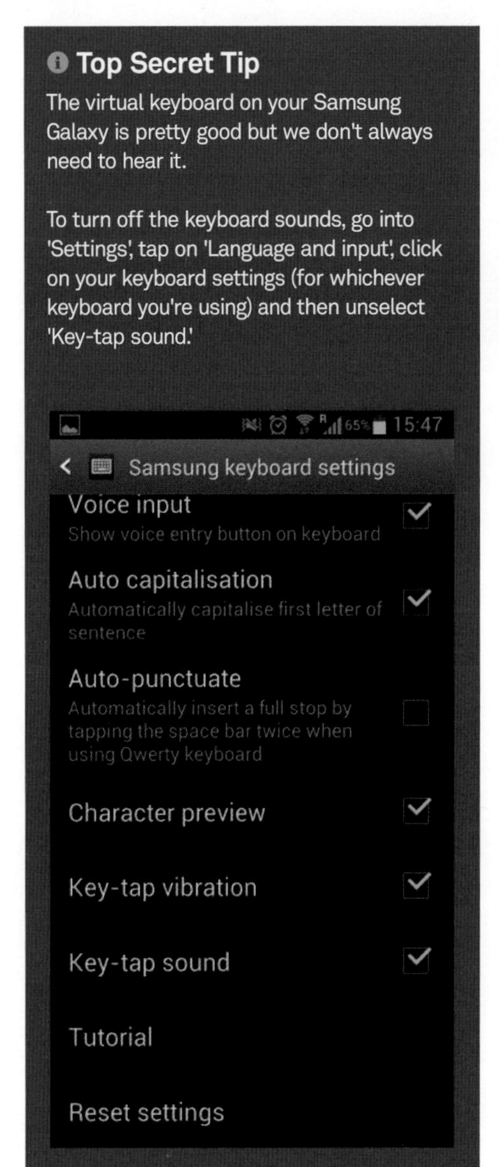

Top Secret Tip

The virtual keyboard on your Samsung Galaxy is pretty good but we don't always need to hear it.

To turn off the keyboard sounds, go into 'Settings', tap on 'Language and input', click on your keyboard settings (for whichever keyboard you're using) and then unselect 'Key-tap sound.'

Samsung really helps you get the most out of its devices by including a few key apps on your Galaxy phone out of the box, with S Note definitely being the most Galaxy Note-centric out there with its intuitive interface, Notebook keeping file organisation and versatile input options.

Creating a Note

- To start your S Note experience tap the app icon and you'll be presented with a number of sample folders. Inside these folders are notebooks, and this main menu is where you can create your own notebooks.

- How? Simply tap the plus icon in the top right-hand corner of the S Note screen. There are a range of templates you can choose from for your note ranging from lined paper, squared paper and a meeting note layout right through to a travel diary or a birthday greeting.

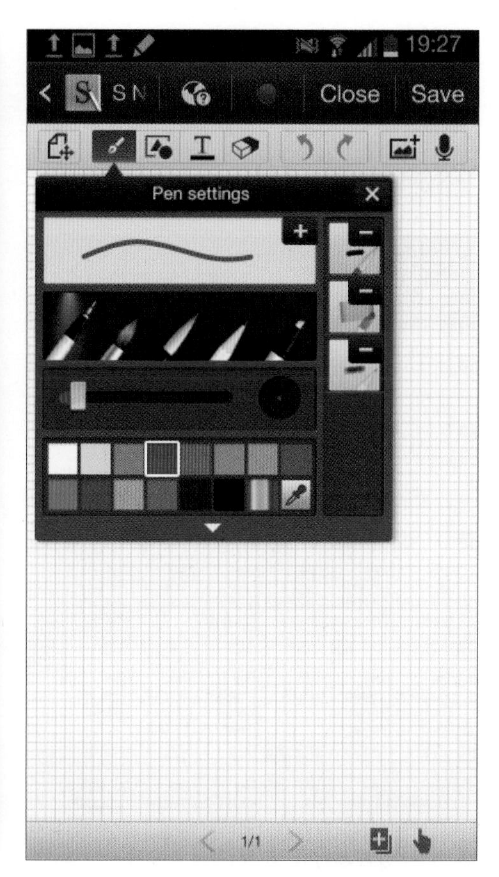

- Once your template is opened up, you're taken straight into edit mode. Here you can draw directly onto the page, make your note and be done with it. If you want to dabble though, you can change your pen thickness, insert images, text and even voice recordings. If you want to change the background to match your note, you can also do this at any point without affecting your handywork.

- The number of options you have will depend on the version of S Note you have, but if you're the proud owner of a Samsung Galaxy Note 2, you'll even be able to go so far as entering formulae and S Note working out the answer.

- We're not even done extolling the virtues of S Note. With your Note created and ready for export, tap your options button, select 'Export' and you'll be able to save your note as either an image file or a PDF to enjoy on your device or share.

S Planner

Another reason Galaxy phones tend to be a cut above most is the on board calendar app, aptly named, S Planner. Available on most Galaxy smartphones and tablets, it takes a tabbed approach to calendars, enabling quick and easy switching between views and comes complete with a fantastic widget.

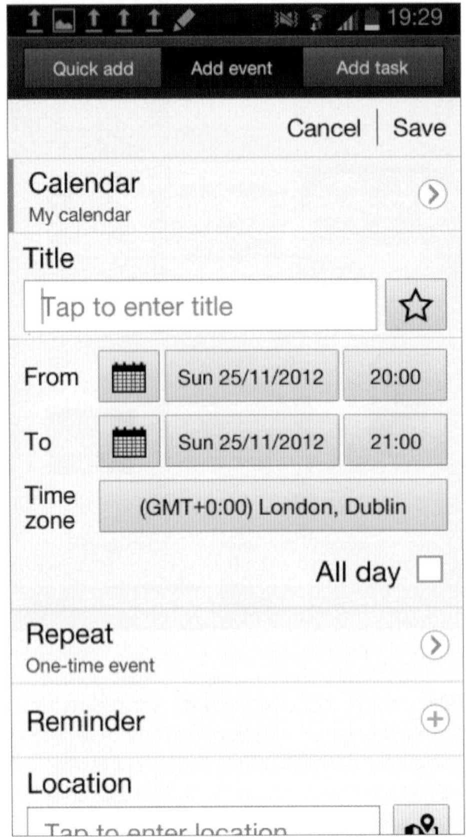

S Planner - App

➲ Located in your application drawer, S Planner will be the default choice for any calendar activity on your Android. This means it will open when you open it or when you interact with another app that uses your calendar.

➲ Once open, the S Planner application contains a number of key elements up at the top. To jump to the present day, just tap the 'Today' icon. If you're looking to toggle which calendars are displayed, tap the 'Calendars' icon. The '+' icon is where you should head when you want to add an event.

➲ Perhaps the most fantastic button in the entire S Planner app, and the one that won our hearts, is the unassuming arrow in the top right. Tapping it is so powerful that it moves the entire screen to the left in order to reveal tabs - wonderful, organised tabs. With year, month week, day, list and task view.

➲ S Note's also a social beast, pulling in all your Facebook birthdays if you let it, so you needn't forget a single one. If you've got a Note 2, you can even write handwritten birthday wishes on your friend's wall on their special day.

S Planner - Widget

➲ As we mentioned, it isn't just the S Planner application that trumps the majority of Androids out there, it's also the S Planner widget. With two available, you can drop a task list of events onto your home screen with the 'S Planner (Mini Today)' widget, but it's the 'S Planner (Month)' widget that won us over.

➲ This big, bold, beautifully clear calendar widget deploys a month view across one full home screen. Each day displays a snippet of your activity and can be clicked through to access the full application. So simple and yet so very good.

S Suggest

The Google Play Store is one phenomenal portal to a world of applications for your Samsung Galaxy device. The Samsung Apps world only adds to this ridiculously rich app ecosystem with a range of exclusive apps, not to mention many available on the Play store. So much choice, but unless you're an Android aficionado, where, oh where, do you begin? S Suggest, that's where.

Top Secret Tip

Google Now is the company's next-generation search engine. It tries to show you the information before you even know you need to search for it. Crazy, huh? It's not perfect, but if you want to give it a try on your Galaxy, simply hold any of the bottom menu buttons (Back, Home or Multitask) and then slide your finger to the top of the circle toward the Google logo.

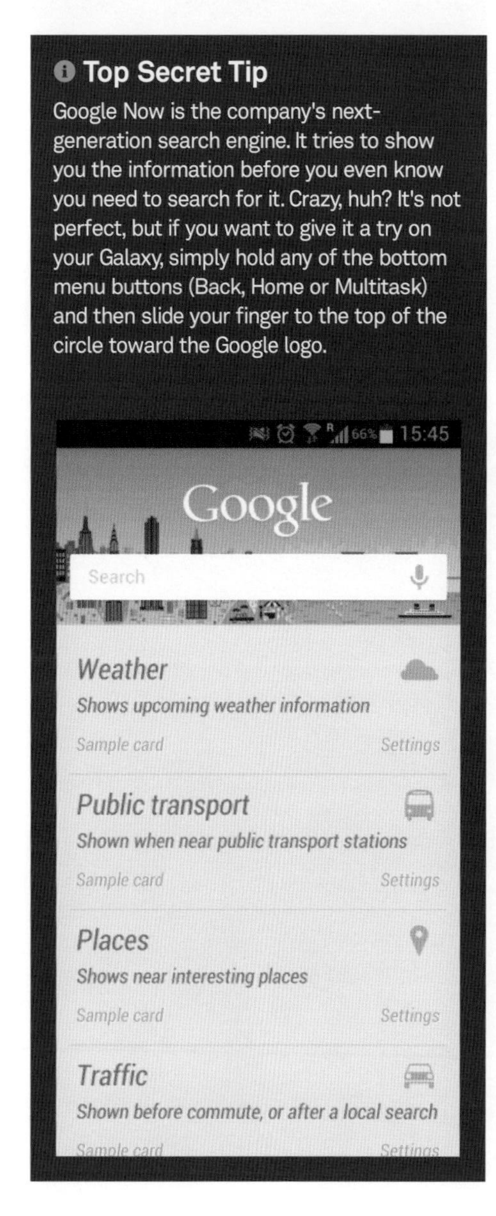

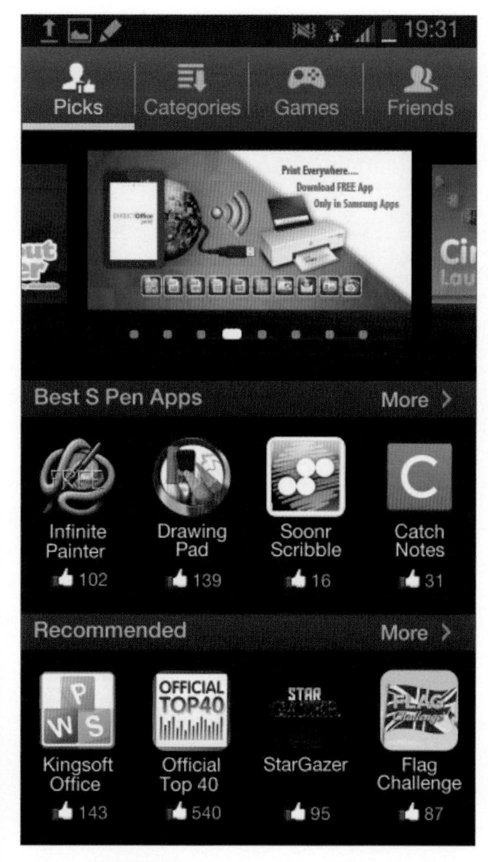

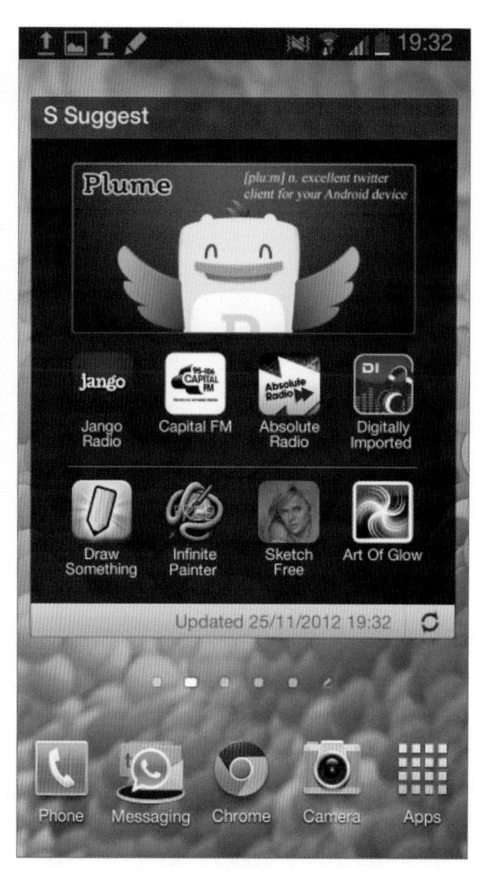

What's S Suggest?

- If the Google Play store is a supermarket, think of S Suggest as a boutique. Curated to save you time and headaches, Samsung suggests applications well suited to your specific device.

- If you have a Samsung Galaxy Note phone or tablet, for example, start up S Suggest and the start screen will have a big old section dedicated to S Pen apps.

- If you want to dig deeper though, you can with ease. Up at the top of the S Suggest screen is a horizontal scrolling bar. With 'Picks' being the start screen, you can also view apps by 'Categories,' 'Games,' 'Friends,' 'Info' and 'Exclusive"

Picks

- If you just want a handful of apps for your device, you needn't venture beyond this start screen. With at least 50 apps accessible, it provides a perfect smorgasbord from which to populate your Galaxy.

Categories

- There's a broad range of categories in S Suggest, just like the Google Play store. What's fantastic about S Suggest's categories though is the obscure categories you won't find collated in the Google Play store. These include 'Kids' to keep your little tech heads entertained and 'Decoration' for anyone who likes to personalise their phones and tabs to the max.

Games

- In much the same way 'Categories' presents multiple categories of apps, so too, 'Games' presents categories of games. All games are pretty much guaranteed to work on your Galaxy. There are even games exclusively free to S Suggest.

- With new apps out every day, there's even an S Suggest widget you can drop onto your homescreen. You need never be behind the curb, whether you make a point of dipping into the S Suggest app or not.

S Voice

Despite voice activation being present on mobiles for more than a decade, it's only of late that it's hogged the limelight once more, becoming a key selling point for the Samsung Galaxy S III in the form of S Voice. Since its debut on the S III, the feature has also made its way on to the Samsung Galaxy Note 2 and Galaxy Mini.

What is S Voice?

It's a voice assistant. Most reliably, you can always depend on S Voice for weather information. Want to make a call or a text? Once more, you can depend on S Voice. It will even open an application with little more than a few choice words and search the web.

Activating and Setting up S Voice

A double tap of the home button of your Galaxy device will turn on S Voice's ears. Before your words can have any effect though, you have to go through a quick setup process. This begins with a step-by-step guide to using the application. Filled with illustrations and useful tid bits, it should give you everything you need to get going.

After activation, S Voice can be opened with either a double tap of home button or an assertive "Hello Galaxy". This wake up command will work from the lock screen and can be customised to a phrase or word of your choosing.

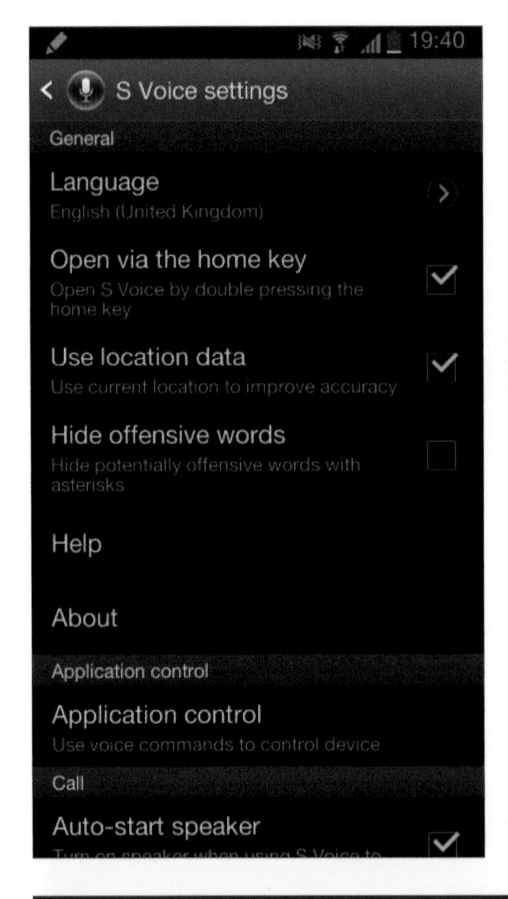

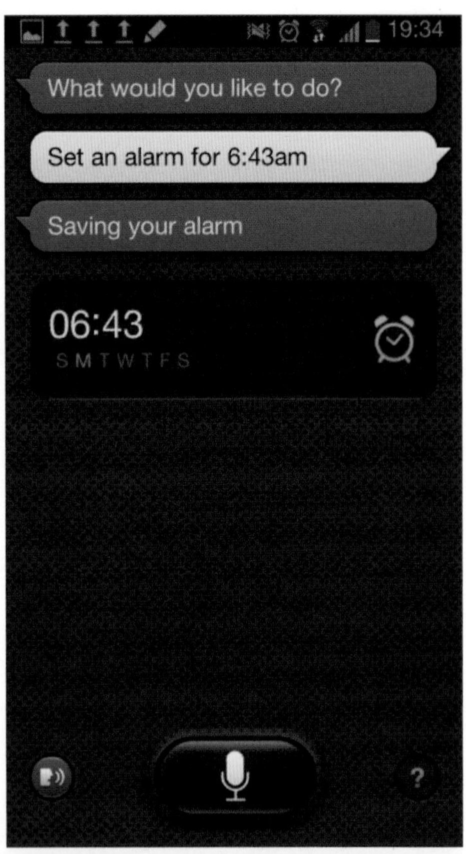

Top Secret Tip

Instead of having to click through to the 'Settings' icon, you can always reach the 'Settings' menu by pulling down the notification bar and then clicking on the 'Settings' icon in the top bar. It's the one that looks like multiple dials, and will take you there no matter what app you're currently in.

You can also instantly turn on/off some features, such as Wi-Fi and GPS.

What commands work with S Voice?

If you want to know if S Voice works with your accent and intonations, ask it the weather. This seems to be the failsafe request when posing a question to Samsung's PA. With full access to the web, you can also use S Voice to search for anything by beginning your question with a "search for". Some other S Voice commands include:

- **"Call [contact name]"** - Dials a contact
- **"Text [contact name, message content]"** - Sends a text message
- **"Look up" [contact name]** - Finds a contact in your phone book
- **"Search [query]"** - Searches Google
- **"Navigate to [place of interest]"** - Activate GPS and Google Navigate
- **"Memo [memo content]"** - Write a memo
- **"New event [event name, date, time]"** - Create an event in S Planner
- **"New task [task name]"** - Adds task to your task-list
- **"Twitter update [tweet content]"** - Updates your Twitter status
- **"Open [application name]"** - Launches an installed application
- **"Set alarm for [time]** - Sets alarm
- **"Set timer for [duration]** - Sets timer
- **"Weather (sample "What is the weather for today?"**
- **"Turn [Wi-Fi/ Bluetooth/ GPS] on/off"** - toggles connectivity setting

S Pen

We've already described the mighty S-Pen as the next evolution of the Stylus and here is where you'll see why. Speaking of evolution, it makes sense to give you a bit of a history lesson as to just how far this little piece of plastic has come.

The Samsung Galaxy Note
We first laid eyes on the S Pen when we got our hands on the original Samsung Galaxy Note. It was the first precise form of pen input for capacitive screens and it blew our minds. We were sold, especially when combined with the ample 5.3-inch screen.

The Samsung Galaxy Note 10.1
Next there was the tablet. The Note 10.1 brought S Pen prodding to 10.1-inches of Galaxy along with a whopping 1024 levels of pressure sensitivity. This means that the in a drawing app for example, the harder you press on the screen, the thicker the line you draw.

The Samsung Galaxy Note 2
The zenith of the Note line, the Samsung Galaxy Note 2 delivers the same incredibly sensitive screen along with a stunning, 5.5-inch HD display and a quad-core processor. It's also loaded with Samsung's Smart Features making it stand out from the crowd even more.

Drawing with the S Pen

The Samsung Galaxy Note range is loaded with the S Planner application. It's a fantastic tool for drawing and takes advantage of the Galaxy Note 2 and Note 10.1's pressure sensitivity. There are a range of brushes to choose from and both handwriting in S Note and doodling are a breeze.

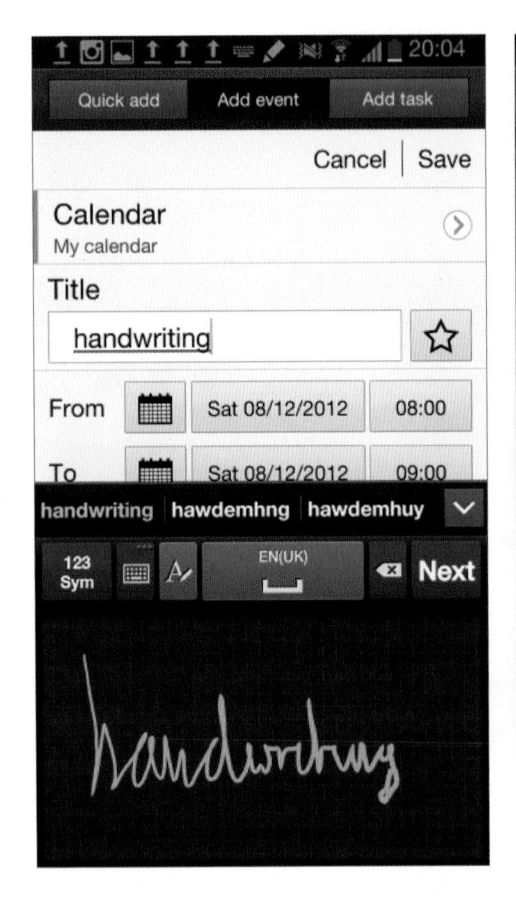

Writing with the S Pen

The Galaxy Note range doesn't just come with souped up styli – oh no. Their keyboards also support handwriting recognition thanks to the precise S Pen. With the stock keyboard set to default, just tap a text entry field while the stylus is un-mounted. This should start up the keyboard in handwriting mode. That failing, just type the T in the bottom left hand corner of the keyboard.

> **Top Secret Tip**
>
> You can launch any app using Quck Commands with the S Pen. Just press the stylus button, swipe up the screen and the Quick commands box will appear. Enter the character you pre-set in the S Pen settings.

The S Pen button

Each S Pen has a button on board. This is another reason it's so much more than just a stylus. With the button held down, for example, draw around an object and you'll lasso around it. The result will be cropped and copied to your Note's clipboard.

The button can also pull up a quick memo with a double tap when held down as well as activate a range of gesture initiated inputs. Add to this extremely accurate handwriting recognition and there's little more we'd think to ask of this mighty piece of plastic.

Airview

With the introduction of the Samsung Galaxy Note 2, the S Pen also grew wings and learnt to hover. This means, without even touching the screen, the Galaxy Note 2 knows the S Pen is near and produces specific information around this hover – or Air View as Samsung calls it.

An example of this would be in your email client. When in the inbox, a simple hover over one of your message previews will pop up a window and show the remainder of the message.

This also works in the S Planner application, gallery and video player to name a few. The truly fantastic, time-saving thing about Airview is that it doesn't open apps and windows it previews completely, it just gives you a peek into them, saving you going back and forth between applications.

Chapter 9

Social

Twitter

140 characters took on a new meaning in March 2006 when the first tweet was published on Twitter by its creator, Jack Dorsey. Now with 500 million users, Twitter is an institution, integrated deeply into smartphones and tablets the world over, your Samsung Galaxy included.

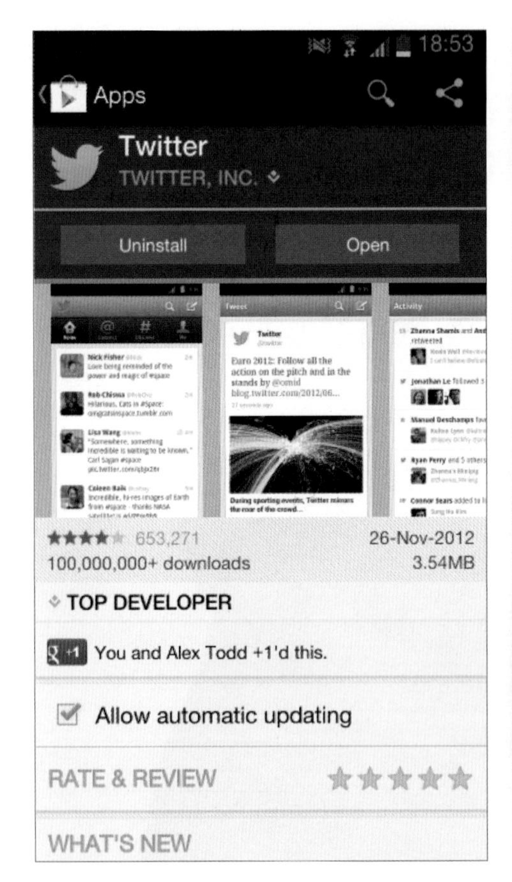

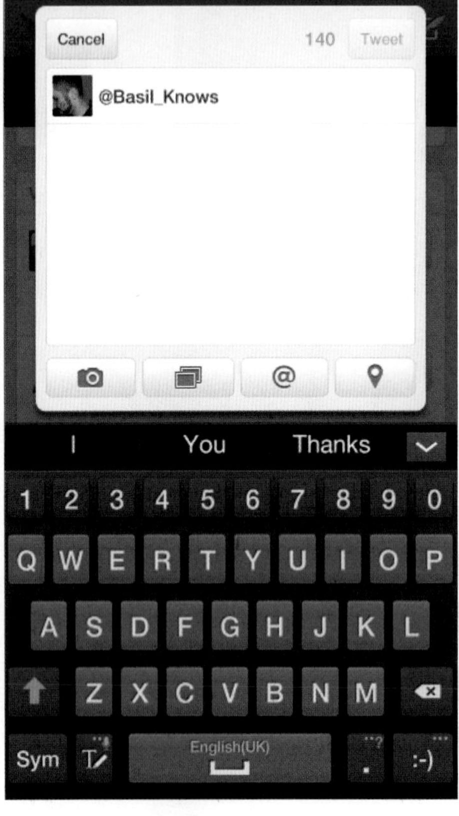

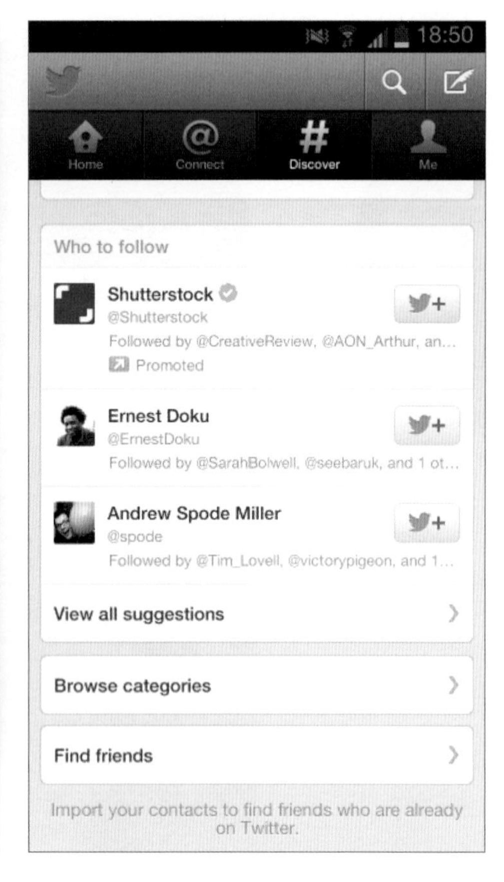

Installing Twitter and creating an account

- The Twitter app isn't preloaded on your Samsung Galaxy Phone out of the box, so to load it up you'll need to download it from the Google Play store. This simply involves opening up the Play store, searching for the Twitter app and hitting 'Install'.

- Once installed and opened, you'll need an account to get going. If you've already got one, just hit 'Sign in' and away you go.

- If you need to create an account, tap 'Sign up'. Fill out the fields required, including your name and email address. Perhaps the most important field to get right is your username. That's what everyone on Twitter will see on your profile and have to type when they send you a tweet, so choose wisely.

Twitter fundamentals

- You're ready and raring to tweet, username or 'Twitter handle' chosen, account setup and profile picture selected. The next step is to add your friends. Fortunately, Twitter's one step ahead of you.

- You'll notice a pop-up asking if you want it to find your friends pretty much straight after it signs you in for the first time. This entails the app scouring your address book, seeing which of your friends are on Twitter and then making following them as easy as possible.

- Friends followed, all that's left to do is get involved. Every time you startup the app, you'll land on your timeline. Here you can see what everyone you follow is tweeting.

- The big '@' symbol up at the top of the screen will take you to all your mentions - instances people have tweeted about you. The '#' next door is where you can discover new people to follow and the final tab, 'Me', is where you can find all your tweets and direct messages. Installing Twitter and creating an account.

Top Secret Tip

To pause a video or song while it's playing without tapping any buttons, put your palm over your Galaxy device and the media will be stopped.

Facebook

If you thought the 500 million users on Twitter was an impressive stat, Facebook has over 500 million active Facebook users on mobile alone. Across phones, tablets and computers, the tally is a whopping 900 million users plus. With Facebook clearly being the socialiser's smartphone 'industry standard', it makes sense we give you a few tips on setting up the big F too.

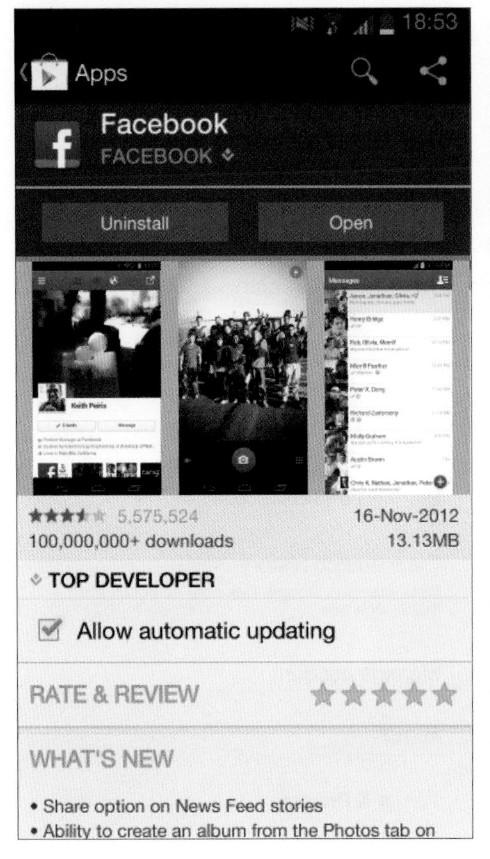

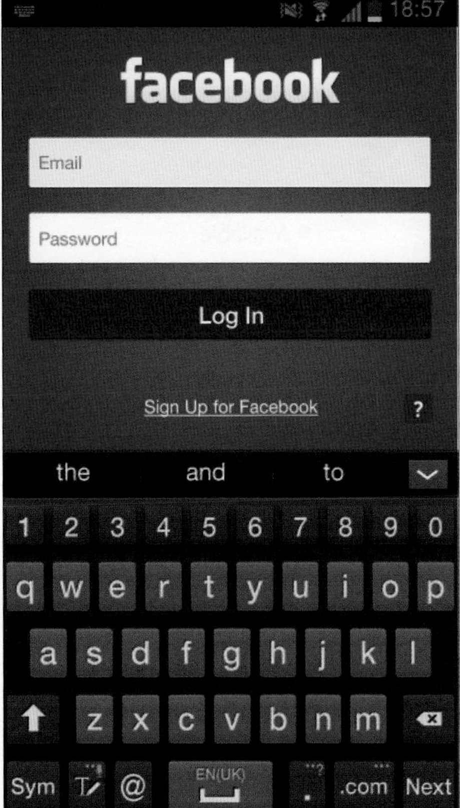

Installing Facebook and creating an account

- Facebook, like Twitter, won't be pre-installed on your Samsung Galaxy smartphone or tablet unless your network has taken the liberty of installing it for you. This means to get Facebooking, you'll have to hop over into your Google Play store once more, search for Facebook and install it.

- Once installed, you'll have to set up a Facebook profile or sign in if you've already got one. Facebook is a bit more comprehensive than Twitter so you might want to make your profile at your desktop.

- Signed in, Facebook will try and sync some stuff with your Samsung Galaxy. Initially giving you the option to sync Facebook contacts with your phonebook though, other syncing items will depend on your tablet.

- If you have a Samsung Galaxy S III or Note 2, for example, you'll want to make sure you're on a Wi-Fi connection. Why? The app will try and pull all your Facebook galleries to your phone's internal storage, be they mere kilobytes or megabytes. Older Galaxy devices needn't fear.

Facebook fundamentals

- The Facebook app itself runs very similarly to the website. It offers three main options up at the top of any given screen. These consist of friend requests, messages and notifications.

- For more options, just tap the three horizontal lines in the top left-hand corner. Here you can access everything to do with your mobile Facebook app, ranging from events and pages through to Facebook apps and even a search bar so you can search for people with ease.

- If you want control of any of the Facebook settings in the future, just tap the menu button on your Galaxy when in the app. Select 'Settings' and you can change what syncs automatically.

Google Talk

Google Talk is the instant messaging service pre-loaded on every Android device out there. That means if you've got a Samsung Galaxy phone or tablet, you've got Google Talk. Didn't know you had it? Just look for Gtalk in your applications list. See - told you it was there.

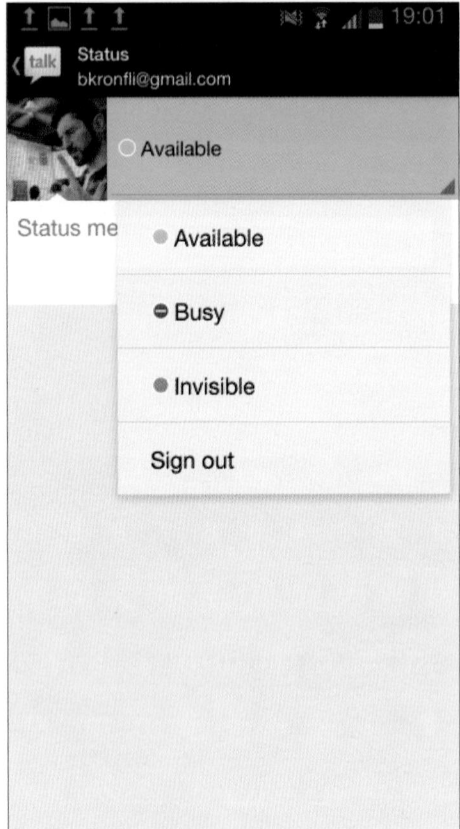

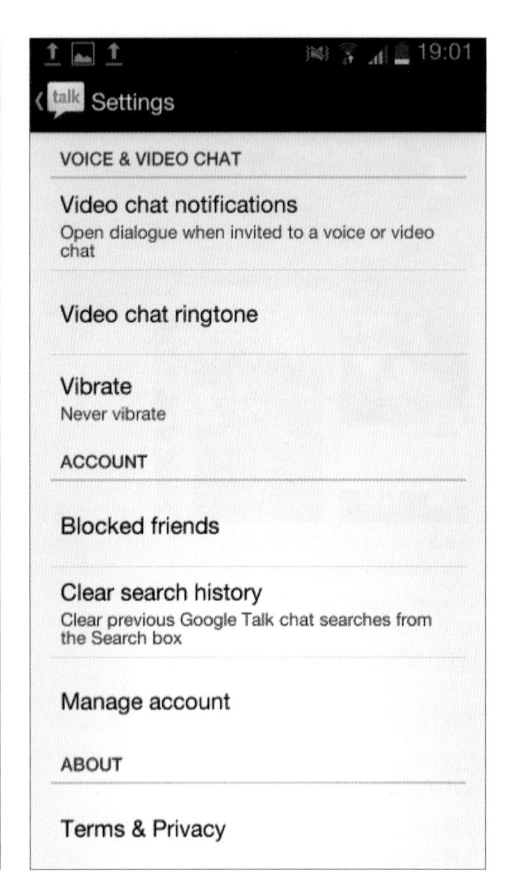

Instant messaging

- Connected to your Gmail account, you won't even need to sign up to Google Talk to get chatting. Just open up the app and away you go. You'll immediately be presented with a list of your contacts who are also signed up to Google's instant messaging service.

- As with other services like Skype and MSN messenger, Google Talk allows you to set statuses, so you can appear available, busy or invisible. To change how you appear, on the main screen just tap your email address which will be at the top of your contacts list.

- To get Google Talk going, just tap on a contact's name and you'll be taken through to a chat window. Your contact's status appears in the form of a coloured ball by their email address. Green means they're 'available', amber means 'away', red means 'busy' and if their profile picture is black and white, they're offline.

Advanced features

- If you've got a list of a hundred or more contacts, scrolling through them can be a pain, but thanks to the search function, you can jump to whichever friend you're looking for with ease. Just tap the magnifying glass in the top right of the app's main contact list.

- If you want to add a contact, it's just as straightforward. You'll see a '+' symbol next to the search icon. This will prompt you enter the email address of whomever you wish to add, after which they'll be sent a chat invite.

- Onto our final Google Talk feature - video calling. Just tap the camera icon next to the respective contact to initiate a video call request. Once they respond, Google chat becomes instantly richer, adding voice and video to its list of communication capabilities. You will need a Galaxy device with a front-facing camera for this last feature to work.

Group Messaging

Unlike the iPhone, Androids in general don't have native group messaging. Gtalk is great for one-on-ones, but you'll have to go elsewhere if you want to natter with multiple chums at once. Fortunately, there are two options and neither will cost you a penny.

Top Secret Tip

Bored of waking up with just a boring alarm? Why not set your Galaxy to read the weather, latest news headlines or your schedule for the day?

To set up the 'Briefing' setting on your Samsung Galaxy device, go to Clock > choose alarm and then head to alarm type, Select 'Briefing' and you can opt for exactly what you want to wake you up.

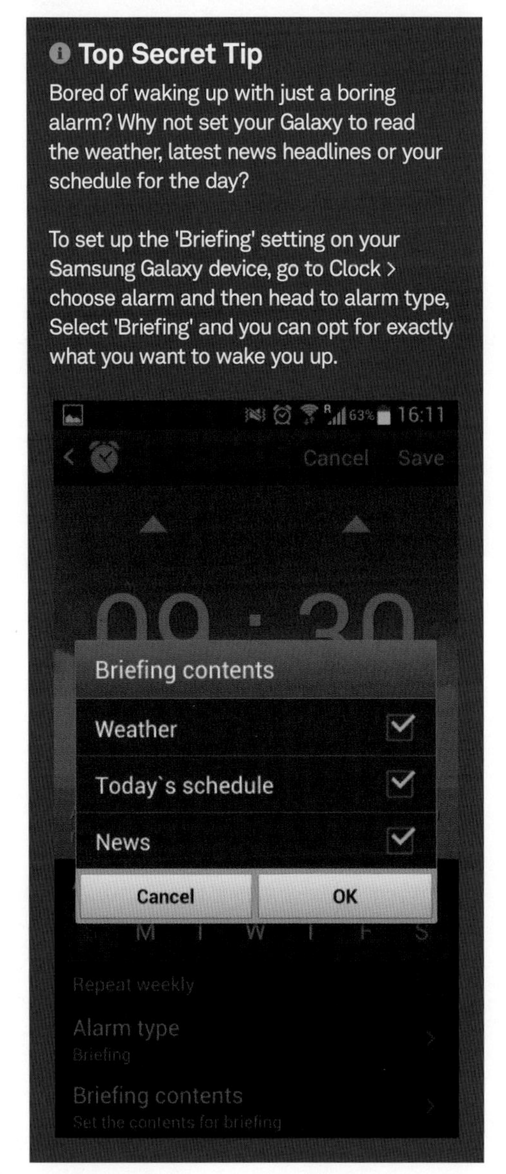

Samsung ChatOn

- Samsung's chat app, ChatOn is pre-installed on all Galaxy Smartphones.
- You'll find the app nested in your apps list and probably sitting pretty as a default lock screen shortcut too.
- When you first open it up, ChatOn prompts you to enter your number, then goes onto verify that you are indeed you. Once done, you'll be treated to a list of all your contacts registered on ChatOn and you can get to group talking with any at your will.
- To do so, just press the menu button on your Galaxy device. The second option should read ' Add group'. Tap that, enter a group name and fill in who you want to be privy to a group invite.
- Given the fact ChatOn only works for Galaxy smartphones, while perfect for a household of Samsung owners. this might not be the best option for chatting with chums who use iPhones and Windows Phones, or even other Android devices.

Whatsapp

- For such users, we present Whatsapp. The cross-platform messaging service is nice and rich like ChatOn, supporting group chats and sound and image sharing. It's also free for Android users which always ups the appeal.
- In the same way ChatOn requires you register your number, so too does Whatsapp. Once registered, the app scours your phonebook for contacts who are using the service already. Being such a popular service, you'll likely find most of your smartphone savvy friends are on it already.
- Once signed up, setting up a group is a piece of cake. Just press of the menu button while on the main screen, tap the 'New Group icon' and select the friends you want to group chat with. Once created, each group can have its own thumbnail and name, you can share files across the entire group and even leave the group when the conversation's over.

Skype

Whatsapp may be cross-platform, working across Android, BlackBerry OS, iOS, Symbian and Windows Phone, but it isn't without its limitations - it doesn't support video calling or communicate with desktops as well as phones. For that type of functionality, you might suggest Google Talk. Even that isn't going to meet all our needs though...

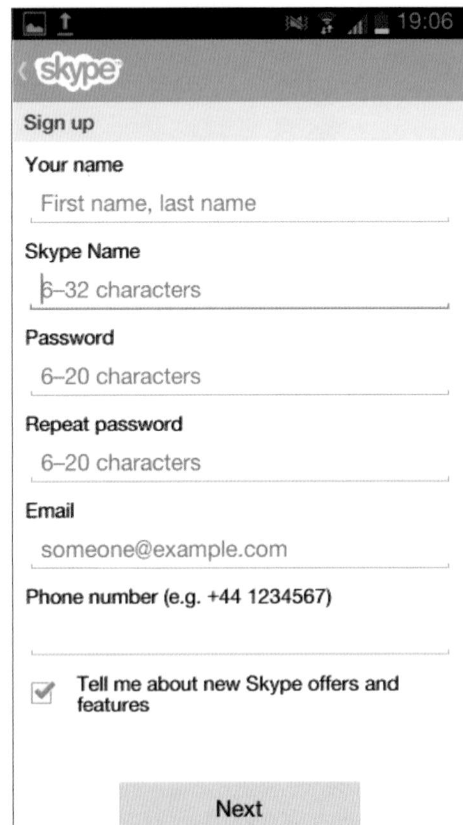

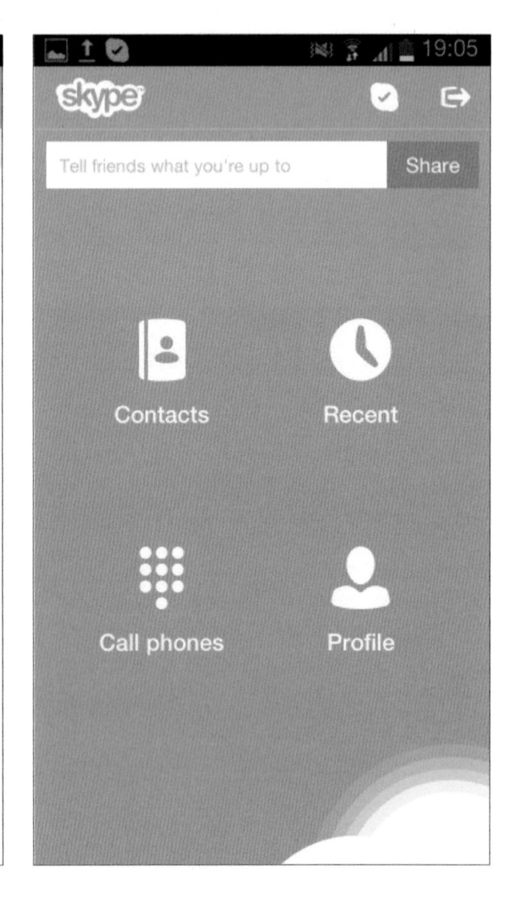

Typically associated with desktop, Skype has apps that work across all major mobile operating systems as well, Android included. With a tablet optimised app introduced towards the end of 2012, whether you're using your Galaxy S II, S III or Tab 10.1, you can get a polished experience with this free app.

Top Secret Tip

Did you know many Samsung Galaxy devices feature a flashlight pre-installed, so you can find your way in the dark?

Just tap the 'Assistive Light' widget to switch on the camera's flash instantly.

Installation and setup

- To get in on the Android Skype action, just search for Skype in the Google Play Store. The app is over 14MB, so you might want to make sure you're connected to a Wi-Fi network when downloading.

- If you don't already have a Skype account setup, you can make one on your Galaxy in a flash, or sign in with your Microsoft account. To create a Skype account, select the create account option from the startup screen. Enter a few details such as your name, email address and phone number, choose a username and password and you're ready to go.

Navigating Skype

- Once signed in, the main screen gives you four main options: Contacts, Recent, Call phones and Profiles.

- Contacts is where you can search all your contacts and choose who to message, video or voice call. Recent is a shortcut to recent chats. Call phones is where you dial phone numbers using your Skype credit and profile is where you can amend your account details.

- You can change your settings by tapping the menu button, then selecting settings. To change your status, press the blob in the top right. Finally, when you're done with Skype and want to sign out, hit the exit button in the top right-hand corner. We'd recommend signing out to preserve your precious battery.

People + Top social apps

By now, you've got all the information you need to turn your Samsung Galaxy device into a social butterfly of a smartphone, but if you're looking to go a little deeper into the social side of your smartphone, check out these three apps...

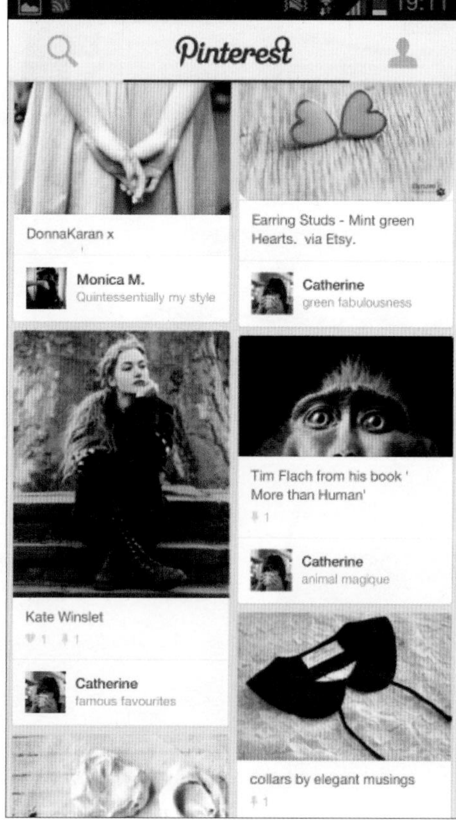

Instagram

- Most phone cameras aren't a patch on dedicated cameras in terms of quality. A grainy out-of-focus shot might prevent you uploading it onto Facebook for fear of embarrassment, but you needn't be so self-conscious. Well, not if you've got Instagram loaded on your Galaxy, that is.

- Loaded with a range of filters that give every image a rustic edge, Instagram is the perfect solution for anyone with a sub-par pixel-count. You can tweak contrast and add some faux depth of field to give even the flattest pictures a sense of dimension. Once done, upload to Twitter and a range of other social networks.

Pinterest

- For the more voyeuristic image lover, Pinterest provides a platform to curate boards rife with images from around the world across a range of subjects. Once you've got an account set up, you can choose your areas of interest and the app will populate a home screen bursting with eye candy. If you want to leave it at that - browsing categories and pinning images to your boards - you can. If, however, you want to take it all a step further, you can easily upload and pin your own images in the hope others will deem them worthy of a precious re-pin.

Foursquare

- If pictures aren't so much your bag, but you're all about your location-based services check out Foursquare. This app lets you check into places and rate, comment or photograph them so, rather than curating visuals, you curate venues. There's also a competitive element to the app as you can become the 'King' of places you frequent more than any other Foursquarer.

Top Secret Tip

Turn the LED indicator alerts on or off by heading to Settings > Display >LED Indicator and choose which options you'd like to activate.

Chapter 10

Maps

Google Maps Overview

As Android devices, all Samsung Galaxy smartphones and tablets come with the Google Maps application pre-installed.

Users must enable location data for it to work properly and although certain elements and services are available offline the majority will require a data connection either through Wi-Fi or 3G/4G on a data plan.

Google Maps supports free turn-by-turn GPS navigation for walking, driving and public transport. It also supports cycle routes, but this is currently in beta, so isn't necessarily bug-free.

You can also use Google Maps to pinpoint your current location, search for addresses, businesses or points of interest (POI) or to share locations, such as where you are currently or a venue for a meeting with your contacts.

There's also a handy new feature that allows you to cache certain map areas for offline use. This is ideal if you're going on holiday or planning a day trip. It's worth noting though this is limited to simply looking at the map: navigation, local searches and other functions won't work without a data connection.

Other features include a 3D view for certain cities, real-time traffic data, and a layers function so you can switch between regular maps, photographic views, terrain, search results, transport routes and traffic.

Google Latitude allows you to share your location with friends so that you can check-in to venues and track each other's movements if you so wish. In some areas, Google Street View also allows you to see what locations look like from the ground level, which can help you find your bearings when visiting somewhere you haven't been to before.

How to activate Google Maps on your Samsung Galaxy device

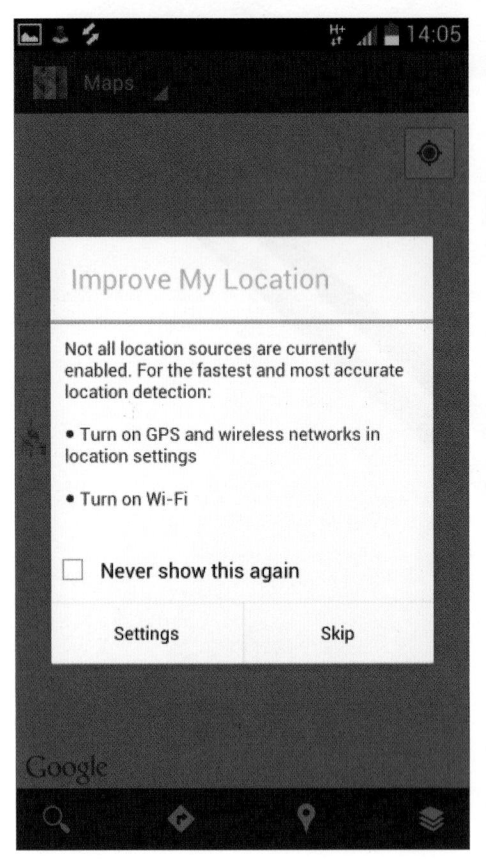

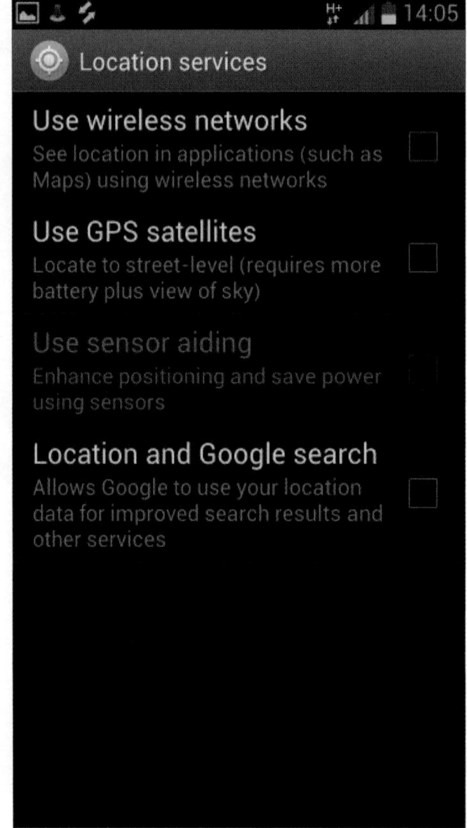

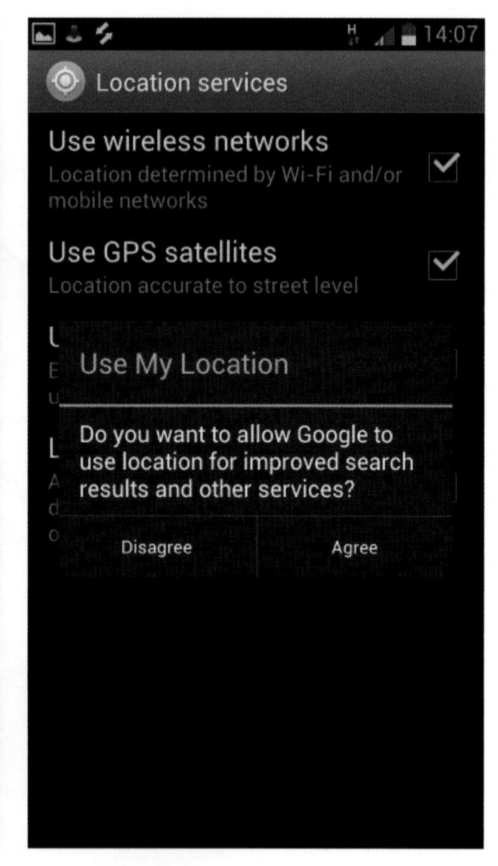

- From the homescreen tap the 'Maps' icon. This may already be on the homescreen or within a folder, but you can always find it by going to the App Drawer, which looks like a small grid of dots and is usually located on the icon bar at the bottom of the screen.
- When you first start Google Maps on your Samsung Galaxy device you should see a message that reads: 'Not all location sources are currently enabled. For the fastest and most accurate location detection: Turn on GPS and wireless networks in location settings'
- You'll then have the option of going straight into the 'Settings' menu to set this up.
- Note that you can independently go into the 'Settings' menu before opening maps to configure location services in advance. To do this tap the 'Settings' icon in the App Drawer and then tap 'Location services'
- In the Location services menu tick the 'Use GPS' checkbox. You'll get a pop-up notification and in order to proceed you'll need to tap 'Agree'.
- You can optionally tick the 'Use wireless networks' checkbox to enable Wi-Fi and mobile data networks. But be warned: the latter may incur charges on your tariff, unless you have an unlimited data plan. To enable this you'll need to agree to any prompts which pop up.
- You can also tick the 'Location and Google search' box to allow Google to use your location data for improved search results.
- You'll now be able to go back into the Maps app and use its various location services.

How to find a POI with Google Maps

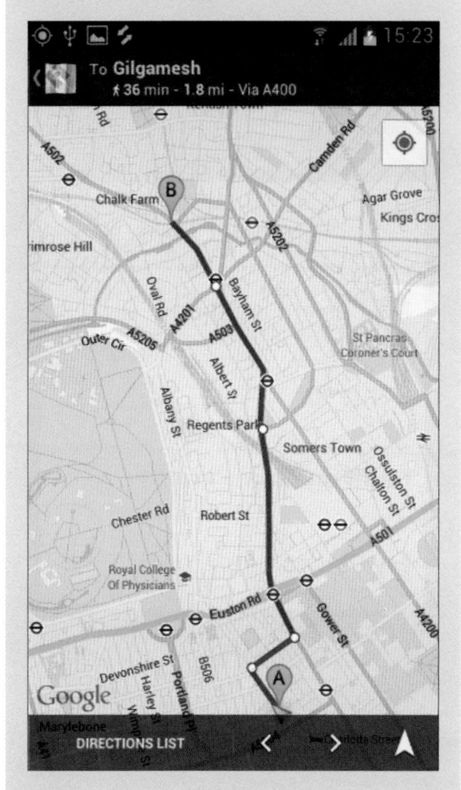

- To find points of interest in Google Maps, start by tapping the 'Places' icon at the bottom of the screen (it resembles an upside-down teardrop shape).
- Select the type of POI you want to find from the options, which include restaurants, coffee shops and many others. Google Maps will take a moment to search and then present you with a list.
- Scroll through to find one you like, then tap on it to be taken to its Maps page.
- To navigate to the location tap 'Directions' and select from the list of transport methods.
- You can also tap 'Map' to view the location on the map. From here tapping on the POI name will take you back to its own Maps page.

How to share your location

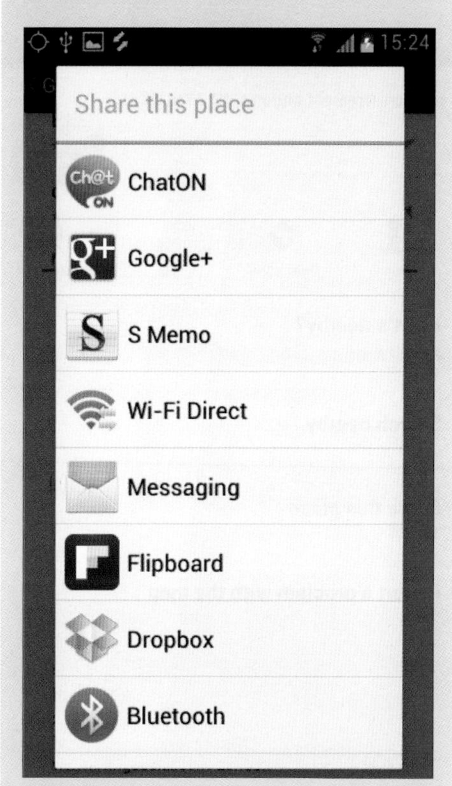

- To share a location, simply scroll to the bottom of the location's page and then tap 'Share this place'.
- A selection of sharing methods will appear, including Facebook, text messaging and email.
- You can also share your current location.
- To do so: Tap on the blue arrow representing your current position, just as you would with a POI.
- Tap the arrow pointing to the right in the pop-up box.
- Tap 'Send location to others' and choose an option from the list.

How to use layers on your Samsung Galaxy

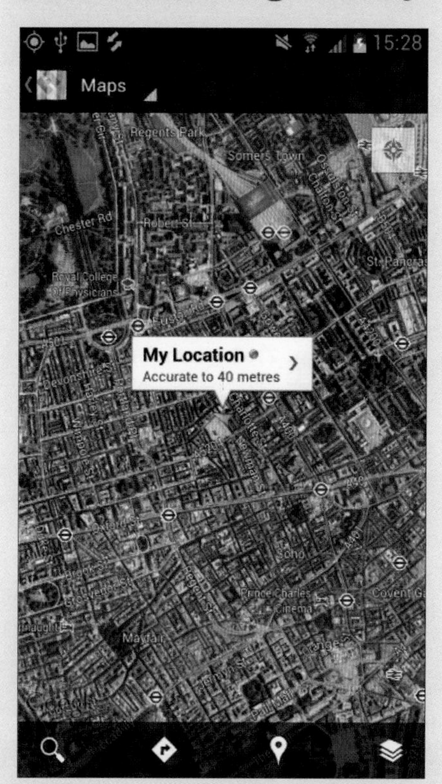

- To use layers just tap the layers icon in the top bar (it looks like a stack of cards).
- From here you can choose from a selection of layer options, including satellite imagery and transport networks.

A note on offline use:
Google Maps supports limited offline use. It will cache areas on the map you've recently viewed so that they're accessible even without a data connection.

With this in mind, it's recommended that if you're going on holiday, say for example to New York, you spend a bit of time exploring the city on Google Maps before you leave so that it caches the data.

You still won't be able to use navigation or many other services without a data connection - which may prove costly - but you can at least look at the map to get your bearings.

How to plot a route with Google Maps

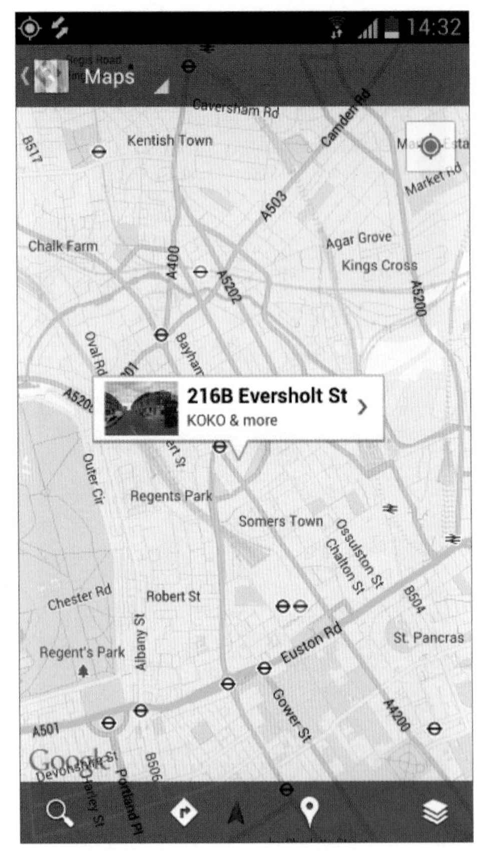

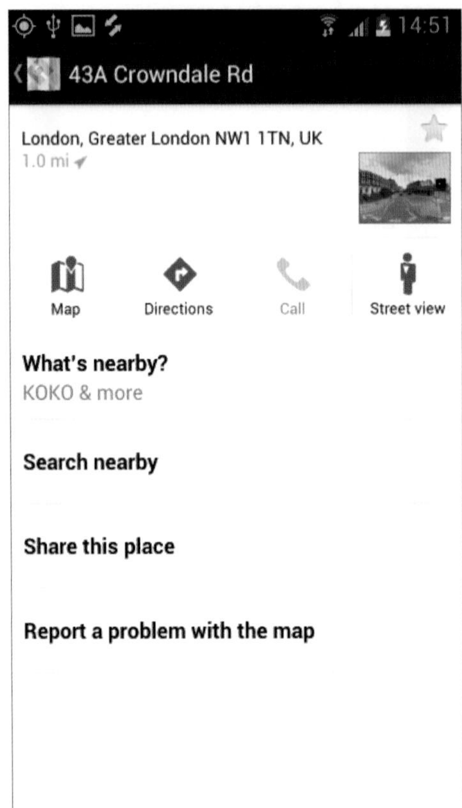

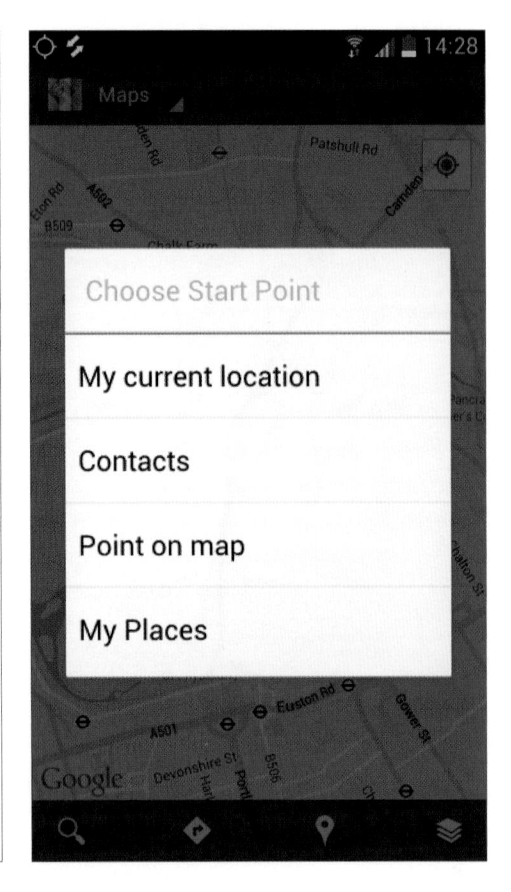

The most basic and frequently used functionality of Google Maps is its turn-by-turn navigation.

Have Google Maps find your current location by pressing the 'Centre on my location' icon (it resembles a dot in the middle of a crosshair). It may take anything from a few seconds to several minutes to find you.

You can either use your current location as a starting point for a route, or you can set one manually with an address, postcode or POI name.

- The easiest way to plot a route is to tap and hold on a point at the map, such as Trafalgar Square (which you can locate by searching in the search bar or panning across the map manually).
- The name of the location should pop up, along with an arrow pointing to the right.
- Tap this arrow then tap the 'Directions' button.
- From the menu that pops up select from the navigation methods (Driving, Walking etc).
- You can tap 'Get Directions' to get the route directly within Google Maps or you can tap 'Navigation' to load the Navigation screen with voiced turn-by-turn directions.
- For an alternative setup, you can tap the 'Directions' button (which resembles a road sign indicating a right turn) to enter details manually.
- The top bar is your starting point, which by default should be set as your current location ('My Location'). Tap here if you want to type an address or postcode, or you can tap the triangular-shaped icon to the right to choose from 'My current location', 'Contacts' or 'Point on map' or saved locations under 'My Places'.
- You may then do the same with the end point bar.
- Then select the transport method from the row of icons (Driving, Walking etc).
- To finish programming the route and begin navigating, tap either 'Navigation' or 'Get Directions', as outlined above.

Chapter 11

Accessories

Samsung D980 Multimedia desktop dock

RRP £25.99

Want to set-up your tablet for multimedia, whether watching films, TV or anything else on the move? The Samsung Multimedia tablet dock positions your tablet at a perfect viewing angle, with a 3.5mm headphone/speaker jack and HDMI out for hooking up to your TV.

Samsung HM3500 Bluetooth headset

RRP £69.99

Samsung's premium Bluetooth headset includes a number of extra features, putting it head and shoulders above the competition. You can connect to two devices at a time and use the headset to stream music. What's more, with noise reduction and echo cancellation, sound is crystal clear.

Samsung Galaxy S III flip cover

RRP £29.99

Like the Samsung Galaxy Note flip cover, the Galaxy S III leather flip cover is available in a range of colours and replaces your phone's battery cover for a super-secure fit. It keeps the S III nice and slimline while also protecting it from pesky keys or other sharp objects in your pocket or bag.

Samsung Galaxy Tab 10.1 clip-in case

RRP £59.99

This custom-fit Samsung Galaxy Tab 10.1 clip-in case for the largest tablet in Samsung's range is hard wearing and even features a stand for propping up your Tab when watching video content. There are holes for all the ports and a secure closing mechanism for added protection.

Samsung Galaxy Note flip case

RRP £29.99

Keep your tablet free from scrapes and bumps with the official Samsung Galaxy Note flip case. The case attaches to your device by replacing the back cover of the handset. It's available in a range of colours too, so you can choose one to suit your mood.

Samsung ET-S200 stylus pen

RRP £19.99

Samsung Galaxy devices are designed to be used with your finger, but if you'd like a little more precision when using your phone or tablet, why not pick up a stylus? This particular accessory offers a comfortable grip and lanyard so you can always have it to hand.

Samsung Galaxy Tab 10.1 desktop dock

£24.99

The desktop dock for Samsung's 10.1-inch tablet puts your device in a perfect viewing position, whether you're watching a film, browsing the web or playing a game. While docked, your tablet will also charge. You can connect audio devices and play your music through the device too.

Samsung Galaxy Tab 8.9 keyboard case

RRP £97.99

The Samsung Galaxy Tab 8.9 is a productivity boosting device and the Galaxy Tab 8.9 keyboard case ensures you can work when you're on the move. The leather case connects via Bluetooth and is both protective and functional.

Samsung microUSB to HDMI cable

RRP £29.99

View all your media on the big screen with Samsung's official HDMI cable, which is compatible with any Samsung device with a microUSB port. It connects from the microUSB port to your TV. Just change your TV's mode to HDMI and you can view anything on your TV.

Samsung K10UWE keyboard dock

RRP £54.99

If you're planning on using your tablet as a computer, or for sending lots of emails, you'll probably find a keyboard useful. Samsung's K10UWE keyboard dock also charges your 7-inch tablet and if you like to listen to music while you type, there's a 3.5mm headphone jack too.

Samsung Galaxy Tab 10.1 leather pouch

RRP £24.99

This simple case protects your Samsung Galaxy Tab without adding much extra bulk. It's perfect for those who carry their Tab in a bag or brief case, where sharp items may scratch the screen. It's also sturdy and made from really soft leather so it looks stylish too.

Samsung universal smartphone desktop dock

RRP £39.99

This clever dock charges your phone with your microUSB charger, keeping it in an upright position so you can browse websites, use apps and message while charging. It features a 3.5mm headphone jack too, so you can listen and control your music at the same time as charging.